Algebra 1

Step By Step Guide

Review for Algebra 1 Book

Plus, Two Algebra 1 Practice Tests

By

Elise Baniam & Michael Smith

Algebra 1 Step-by-Step Guide

Published in the United State of America By

The Math Notion Inc

Email: info@mathnotion.com

Web: www.mathnotion.com

ISBN: 978-1-63620-220-4

About the Author

Meet **Elise Baniam**, a celebrated math author with a passion for educating students of all ages. Elise has devoted her career to writing mathematics books that are both engaging and informative.

Elise's journey began when she earned a bachelor's degree in mathematics from a university. Since then, she has authored numerous books covering a broad range of topics, from elementary to advanced mathematics. Elise's books are renowned for their accessibility, making complex concepts simple to understand while still challenging students to think creatively.

In addition to writing books, Elise is an active member of the mathematics community. She attends conferences and workshops regularly, staying abreast of the latest teaching techniques and innovations. Elise also enjoys volunteering her time to mentor aspiring mathematicians.

Overall, Elise is a dedicated and accomplished math author who is passionate about making math accessible to everyone. Her books have helped countless students around the world develop a love for math and achieve success in the subject.

You can contact Elise via email at:

Elise@mathnotion.com

Unlocking the Mysteries of Algebra with Ease!

Are you looking to resolve the complexities of algebra without getting overwhelmed? Your search ends here! Getting on the journey into the world of algebra can often be daunting. With the right guide, the complex becomes clear, the intricate simple. "Algebra 1 Step by Step Guide" is accurately designed to be that essential companion, making the path to algebraic mastery both achievable and enjoyable.

Crafted by a team of expert educators with decades of experience, this guide breaks down algebraic concepts into easily understandable components, offering over 2,500 practice problems that cover the depth subjects of Algebra 1. Whether you're a student grappling with quadratic equations or an adult looking to refresh your algebraic skills, this book assists as an encouragement, illuminating the way.

Features of the guide:

- ✓ **Comprehensive Coverage:** All foundational topics of Algebra 1 are presented in a structured manner.

- ✓ **Diverse Practice Problems:** Engage with a mix of problems that range from basic to challenging, ensuring a well-rounded grasp.

- ✓ **Step-by-Step Solutions:** Understand the 'why' behind every problem, aiding in concept retention.

- ✓ **Strategic Tips and Tricks:** Learn effective techniques to solve problems quicker and more accurately.

- ✓ **Self-Assessment Tools:** Two full-length practice tests to gauge your progress and readiness.

- ✓ **User-Friendly Layout:** Clearly defined sections, summaries, and ample workspace for practice.

With this book in hand, algebraic fluency is not just a goal, but an assured achievement. Presenting the book, a precisely crafted resource that is dedicated to simplifying algebra for every learner, regardless of their prior knowledge.

Dive in and discover the joy of understanding and mastering Algebra 1.

WWW.MATHNOTION.COM

… So Much More Online!

✓ FREE Math Lessons

✓ More Math Learning Books!

✓ Mathematics Worksheets

✓ Online Math Tutors

For a PDF Version of This Book

Please Visit www.mathnotion.com

How to properly use the book?

Using the step-by-step guidebook, like one for Algebra 1, effectively can make a significant difference in understanding and mastering the subject. Here are some steps and strategies to get the most out of your Algebra 1 study guidebook:

1) **Familiarize Yourself with the Contents:**

   - Scan through the entire book to get an overview of the topics covered.

   - Take note of the structure. Are there chapters, sections, examples, and solutions?

2) **Set Clear Goals:**

   - Determine what you want to achieve. Is it a better understanding of a particular topic, exam preparation, or just general knowledge enrichment?

   - Break your goals down into smaller, manageable tasks.

3) **Plan Your Study Time:**

   - Allocate specific times for studying. Consistency can help reinforce learning.

   - Avoid cramming. Spread your study sessions out over time.

4) **Active Reading:**

   - Don't just passively read. Engage with the content.

   - Highlight key points, make annotations, and jot down summaries.

5) **Work Through Practice Problems:**

   - The essence of algebra is problem-solving. Make sure to work through the practice problems in the guidebook.

   - After attempting problems, check the solutions. If you get something wrong, understand why.

6) **Use Additional Resources:**

   - If there's a concept you're struggling with, seek additional resources like online videos, tutorials, or other textbooks. Sometimes a different explanation can make things click.

7) Review Regularly:

- Periodic review helps reinforce what you've learned.

- Revisit challenging topics or problems you initially got wrong.

8) Study Actively and Engage Multiple Senses:

- Explain difficult concepts aloud as if you're teaching someone else.

- Draw diagrams or use physical objects to represent algebraic concepts.

9) Join a Study Group:

- Discussing and teaching topics can solidify your understanding.

- Other students might have insights or understanding that you haven't considered.

10) Seek Help When Needed:

- Don't be afraid to ask for help if you're stuck.

- This could be from a teacher, tutor, classmate, or online forum.

11) Test Yourself:

- If your guidebook has quizzes or mock exams, take them seriously.

- This helps gauge your understanding and readiness for any actual exams.

12) Stay Curious and Relate to Real Life:

- Try to relate algebraic concepts to real-world applications. This not only makes it more interesting but can also aid understanding.

Remember, the key is consistency and active engagement. With regular, focused effort and the right strategies, you can use your Algebra 1 study guidebook to its full potential and master the subject.

Contents

Chapter 1 : Review the Basics

 Mathematical concepts covered:

- ◉ Adding and Subtracting Integers
- ◉ Multiplying and Dividing Integers
- ◉ Order of Operations
- ◉ Integers and Absolute Value
- ◉ The Distributive Property
- ◉ Approximating Irrational Numbers
- ◉ Scientific Notation
- ◉ Addition and Subtraction in Scientific Notation
- ◉ Multiplication and Division in Scientific Notation
- ◉ Finding Midpoint

Adding and Subtracting Integers

Integers cover zero, positive counting numbers, and the negations of those counting numbers. The integer set is represented as {..., -3, -2, -1, 0, 1, 2, 3, ...}.

To increase a number, you move to the right on the number line by adding a positive integer. This results in a larger number.

On the other hand, to decrease a number, you move to the left on the number line by adding a negative integer. This leads to a smaller number.

Subtracting an integer is equivalent to adding its opposite.

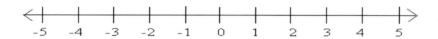

Examples:

1) Solve: $6 + (9 - 5)$

   Solution: First, subtract the numbers in brackets, $9 - 5 = 4$.

   Then: $6 + 4 = 10$.

2) Solve: $(-7) - (-3)$.

   Solution: Keep the first number and convert the sign of the second number to its opposite. Change subtraction into addition.

   Then: $(-7) + 3 = -4$.

3) Solve: $(16 - 8) + 12$

   Solution: First, subtract the numbers in brackets, $16 - 8 = 8$.

   Then: $8 + 12 = 20$.

4) Solve: $5 + (-7 - 3)$

   Solution: First, subtract the numbers in brackets, $-7 - 3 = -10$.

   Then: $5 + (-10) = -5$.

Multiplying and Dividing Integers

Use the following rules for multiplying and dividing integers:

❖ $(negative) \times (negative) = positive$

❖ $(negative) \div (negative) = positive$

❖ $(negative) \times (positive) = negative$

❖ $(negative) \div (positive) = negative$

❖ $(positive) \times (positive) = positive$

❖ $(positive) \div (negative) = negative$

Examples:

1) Solve: $5 \times (-2)$

   Solution: Using the rule (positive) × (negative) = negative.

   $5 \times (-2) = -10$.

2) Solve: $(-6) + (-15 \div 3)$

   Solution: First, divide -15 by 3, using the rule (negative) ÷ (positive) = negative.

   $(-15) \div 3 = -5$. Then, $(-6) + (-5) = -11$.

3) Solve: $(9 - 7) \times (-3)$

   Solution: First, subtract the numbers in brackets, $9 - 7 = 2 \rightarrow (2) \times (-3)$.

   Now, using the rule (positive) × (negative) = negative, $(2) \times (-3) = -6$.

4) Solve: $(10 - 4) \div (-2) =$

   Solution: First, subtract the numbers in brackets, $10 - 4 = 6 \rightarrow (6) \div (-2)$.

   Now, using the rule (positive) ÷ (negative) = negative, $(6) \div (-2) = -3$.

Order of Operations

In the field of Mathematics, we refer to "operations" as addition, subtraction, multiplication, division, exponentiation (represented as b^n) and grouping.

To simplify expressions involving multiple operations, the acronym PEMDAS can be used as a guide: (To remember this rule, recall the phrase "Please Excuse My Dear Aunt Sally".)

- ❖ Parentheses
- ❖ Exponents
- ❖ Multiplication and Division (from left to right)
- ❖ Addition and Subtraction (from left to right)

Examples:

1) Calculate: $(3 + 4) \div (3^2 \div 9) =$

    Solution: First, simplify inside parentheses:

    $(7) \div (9 \div 9) = (7) \div (1)$. Then: $(7) \div (1) = 7$.

2) Calculate: $-3[(2 \times 6) \div (4 \times 3)] =$

    Solution: First, simplify inside the parentheses:

    $-3[(12) \div (4 \times 3)] = -3[(12) \div (12)] = -3$

    multiply -3 and 1. Then: $-3[1] = -3$.

3) Calculate: $(36 \div 6) + (-15 + 2) =$

    Solution: First, calculate within parentheses:

    $(36 \div 6) + (-15 + 2) = (6) + (-13)$. Then: $(6) - (13) = -7$

4) Calculate: $(7 \times 3) - (11 - 5) =$

    Solution: First, calculate within parentheses:

    $(7 \times 3) - (11 - 5) = (21) - (6)$. Then: $(21) - (6) = 15$.

Integers and Absolute Value

The concept of absolute value refers to the distance of a number from zero, regardless of its positive or negative sign, on the number line. For instance, both 9 and -9 are situated 9 units away from zero on the number line.

The absolute value of an integer is the numerical value of the number without considering its sign, whether it is negative or positive.

To denote absolute value, we use vertical bars, such as $|x|$.

It's important to note that the absolute value of a number is always non-negative since it solely indicates the "distance" of the number from zero.

Examples:

1) Calculate: $|10 - 6| \times 3$.

First, solve $|10 - 6|, \rightarrow |10 - 6| = |4|$,the absolute value of 4: $|4| = 4$.

Finally, $4 \times 3 = 12$.

2) $|9 - 4| \times \frac{|-5 \times 6|}{3} =$

Solution: First, solve $|9 - 4|, \rightarrow |9 - 4| = |5|$,

the absolute value of 5 is 5, $|5| = 5$. Then: $5 \times \frac{|-5 \times 6|}{3}$. Then: $5 \times 10 = 50$.

3) $\frac{|-64|}{8} \times |4 - 6|$

Solution: First, find $|-64| \rightarrow$ the absolute value of -64 is 64.

Then: $|-64| = 64, \frac{64}{8} \times |4 - 6| =$.

Now, calculate $|4 - 6|, \rightarrow |4 - 6| = |-2|$,

the absolute value of -2 is 2: $|-2| = 2$. Then: $\frac{64}{8} \times 2 = 8 \times 2 = 16$.

The Distributive Property

The distributive property, also known as the distributive property of multiplication over addition and subtraction, simplifies and solves expressions in the form of:

$$a(b + c) \text{ or } a(b - c).$$

It involves multiplying a term outside the parentheses by the terms inside.

The Distributive Property rule states: $a(b + c) = ab + ac$; or $a(b - c) = ab - ac$

Examples:

1) Simply using the distributive property: $(-4)(x + 2)$

   Use the Distributive Property rule:

   $$(-4)(x + 2) = (-4 \times x) + (-4) \times (2) = -4x - 8$$

2) Example 2: Simply using the distributive property: $(-6)(-3x - 7)$

   Use the Distributive Property rule: $a(b + c) = ab + ac$.

   $(-6)(-3x - 7) = (-6) \times (-3x) + (-6) \times (-7) = 18x + 42$.

3) Example 3: Simply using the distributive property $(5)(4x - 9) - 3x$

   First, simplify $(5)(4x - 9)$ using the distributive property.

   Then: $(5)(4x - 9) = 20x - 45$.

   Now combine like terms: $(5)(4x - 9) - 3x = 20x - 45 - 3x$.

   In this expression, 20x and -3x are "like" terms and we can combine them. $20x - 3x = 17x$. Then: $20x - 45 - 3x = 17x - 45$.

4) Example 4: Simply using the distributive property: $(-2)(2x + 5) + 6x$

   First, simplify $(-2)(2x + 5)$, using the distributive property.

   Then: $(-2)(2x + 5) = -4x - 10$. Now combine like terms:

   $(-2)(2x + 5) + 6x = -4x - 10 + 6x$.

   In this expression, $-4x$ and $6x$ are "like" terms and we can combine them.

   $-4x + 6x = 2x$. Then: $-4x - 10 + 6x = 2x - 10$.

Approximating Irrational Numbers

Numbers that cannot be expressed as fractions are referred to as irrational. These numbers are distinguished by their non-repeating, non-terminating decimal nature, and they do not use a precise spot on the number line. When you take the square root of a number that is not a perfect square, the result is an irrational number.

To approximate an irrational number, we represent its value using rational numbers as closely as possible. This allows us to visually determine its position on a number line diagram. The goal is to determine a value that is as close to the true value of the irrational number as is necessary for our needs.

Examples:

1) Find the approximation of $\sqrt{3}$.

   Given that 3 is not a perfect square, $\sqrt{3}$ is irrational. To approximate $\sqrt{3}$, first, we need to find the two consecutive perfect squares that 3 is between. We can do this by writing this inequality: $1 < 3 < 4$. Now take the square root of each number: $\sqrt{1} < \sqrt{3} < \sqrt{4}$. Simplify the square roots of perfect squares: $1 < \sqrt{3} < 2$, then $\sqrt{3}$ is between 1 and 2. To find a more precise approximation, let's select some decimal values within this range.

   Let's choose 1.5, 1.6, and 1.7 → $1.5^2 = 2.25$, $1.6^2 = 2.56$, $1.7^2 = 2.89$, 2.89 is closer to 3. Then: $\sqrt{3} \approx 1.7$.

2) Find the approximation of $\sqrt{32}$.

   Solution: Since 32 is not a perfect square, $\sqrt{32}$ is irrational.

   25 and 36 are two consecutive perfect squares that 32 is between.

   Then: $25 < 32 < 36 \rightarrow \sqrt{25} < \sqrt{32} < \sqrt{36} \rightarrow 5 < \sqrt{32} < 6$.

   Notice that $\sqrt{32}$ is closer to 5 than 6.

   Try different numbers. Then: $\sqrt{32} \approx 5.7$

Scientific Notation

Scientific notation is a method used to express extremely large or small numbers concisely in decimal format.

Numbers written in scientific notation follow the format: $m \times 10^n$, where the absolute value of m is greater than or equal to 1 and less than 10 ($1 \leq |m| < 10$).

To convert a number from scientific notation to its standard form, shift the decimal point to the left if the exponent of ten is negative (indicating a small number), or to the right if the exponent is positive (indicating a large number).

Examples:

1) Write 0.00068 in scientific notation.

    shift the decimal point to the right to obtain a number between 1 and 10, which is 6.8. Then, identify the number of places the decimal moved, which in this case is 4 places to the right. This becomes the negative exponent of 10, because the decimal moved to the right. So $0.00068 = 6.8 \times 10^{-4}$.

2) Write 2.942×10^{-6} in standard notation.

    Solution: The exponent is -6, so you move the decimal point to the left six places (you can visualize 2.9 as 0000002.942). When the decimal moves to the right, the exponent is negative. Then: $2.942 \times 10^{-6} = 0.000002942$.

3) Write 73,100,000,000 in scientific notation.

    First, move the decimal point to the left so you have a number between 1 and 10. Then: $m = 7.31$. Now, determine how many places the decimal moved in step 1 by the power of 10. $10^{10} \rightarrow$ Then: $73,100,000,000 = 7.31 \times 10^{10}$.

4) Write 8.4×10^6 in standard notation.

    The exponent is 6, so you move the decimal point six places to the right from the number 8.4, adding zeros as necessary.
    Then: $8.4 \times 10^6 = 8,400,000$

Addition and Subtraction in Scientific Notation

To do addition or subtraction operations with numbers in scientific notation, the exponents of the base number of 10 must have the same power:

➤ Step 1: Adjust the exponents of the numbers to make them the same. Typically, it's simpler to match the smaller exponent to the larger one.

➤ Step 2: Perform the addition or subtraction operation on the coefficients.

➤ Step 3: If necessary, adjust the result to ensure it is in proper scientific notation. Remember, the proper form of scientific notation requires that the coefficient (the number part not including the power of ten) must be between 1 and 10.

Examples:

Write the answers in scientific notation.

1) $1.92 \times 10^{12} + 3.8 \times 10^{12}$

Since two numbers have the same power, factor 10^{12} out.

$(1.92 + 3.8) \times 10^{12} = 5.72 \times 10^{12}$.

2) $8.7 \times 10^8 - 6.2 \times 10^8$

Since two numbers have the same power, factor 10^8 out.

$(8.7 - 6.2) \times 10^8 = 2.5 \times 10^8$.

3) $4.8 \times 10^9 + 5.3 \times 10^9$

Since two numbers have the same power, factor 10^9 out.

$(4.8 + 5.3) \times 10^9 = 10.1 \times 10^9$

Now, convert the answer to scientific notation: 1.01×10^{10}.

4) $6.8 \times 10^7 - 2.3 \times 10^6$

Since two numbers haven't the same power, must change to have the same powers. $68 \times 10^6 - 2.3 \times 10^6$; then factor 10^6 out.

$(68 - 2.3) \times 10^6 = 65.7 \times 10^6$; Now, convert the answer to scientific notation: 6.57×10^7.

Multiplication and Division in Scientific Notation

In scientific notation, multiplying two numbers involves multiplying their coefficients and adding their exponents. This method allows us to express the product in a concise form, making calculations and comprehension easier. The result of the multiplication will also be in scientific notation, which is especially useful when dealing with large or small numbers.

Similarly, when dividing two numbers in scientific notation, we divide their coefficients and subtract their exponents.

Examples:

1) Solve $(4.5 \times 10^5)(5 \times 10^{-3})$.

   First, multiply the coefficients: $4.5 \times 5 = 22.5$

   Add the powers of 10: $10^5 \times 10^{-2} = 10^3$.

   Then: $(4.5 \times 10^5)(5 \times 10^{-2}) = 22.5 \times 10^3$

   Now, convert the answer to scientific notation: 2.25×10^4.

2) Find $\frac{3.2 \times 10^{-5}}{8 \times 10^7}$.

   First, divide the coefficients: $\frac{3.2}{8} = 0.4$ (the number must be between 1 and 10)

   Subtract the power of the exponent in the denominator from the exponent in the numerator: $\frac{10^{-5}}{10^7} = 10^{-5-7} = 10^{-12}$. Then: $\frac{3.2 \times 10^{-5}}{8 \times 10^7} = 0.4 \times 10^{-12}$.

   Now, convert the answer to scientific notation: $0.4 \times 10^{-12} = 4 \times 10^{-13}$.

3) Solve $(1.2 \times 10^8)(3 \times 10^7)$.

   First, multiply the coefficients: $1.2 \times 3 = 3.6$

   Add the powers of 10: $10^8 \times 10^7 = 10^{15}$.

   Then: $(1.2 \times 10^8)(3 \times 10^7) = 3.6 \times 10^{15}$

Finding Midpoint

The midpoint of a line segment is the point that divides the segment into two equal parts. If you have a line segment with endpoints at coordinates $((x_1, y_1))$ and $((x_2, y_2))$, the midpoint $((x_m, y_m))$can be found using the following formulas:

$$x_m = \frac{x_1 + x_2}{2} \; ; \; y_m = \frac{y_1 + y_2}{2}$$

❖ For a line segment in three-dimensional space with endpoints at $((x_1, y_1, z_1))$ and $((x_2, y_2, z_2))$, the midpoint can be similarly found:

$$x_m = \frac{x_1 + x_2}{2}; \; y_m = \frac{y_1 + y_2}{2} \; ; \; z_m = \frac{z_1 + z_2}{2}$$

Examples:

1) Find the midpoint of the line segment with the given endpoints. $(3, -5), (7, 10)$

   Midpoint $= \left(\frac{x_1 + x_2}{2}, \frac{y_1 + y_2}{2} \right) \rightarrow (x_1, y_1) = (3, -5)$ and $(x_2, y_2) = (7, 10)$.

   Midpoint $= \left(\frac{3+7}{2}, \frac{-5+10}{2} \right) \rightarrow \left(\frac{10}{2}, \frac{5}{2} \right) \rightarrow M(5, 2.5)$

2) Find the midpoint of the line segment with the given endpoints. $(-3, 4), (7, -8)$

   Midpoint $= \left(\frac{x_1 + x_2}{2}, \frac{y_1 + y_2}{2} \right) \rightarrow (x_1, y_1) = (-3, 4)$ and $(x_2, y_2) = (7, -8)$.

   Midpoint $= \left(\frac{-3+7}{2}, \frac{4+(-8)}{2} \right) \rightarrow \left(\frac{4}{2}, \frac{-4}{2} \right) \rightarrow M(2, -2)$.

3) Find the midpoint of the line segment with the given endpoints. $(8, -5), (2, 9)$

   Midpoint $= \left(\frac{x_1 + x_2}{2}, \frac{y_1 + y_2}{2} \right) \rightarrow (x_1, y_1) = (8, -5)$ and $(x_2, y_2) = (2, 9)$.

   Midpoint $= \left(\frac{8+2}{2}, \frac{-5+9}{2} \right) \rightarrow \left(\frac{10}{2}, \frac{4}{2} \right) \rightarrow M(5, 2)$.

4) Find the midpoint of the line segment with the given endpoints. $(9, -6), (3, 8)$

   Midpoint $= \left(\frac{x_1 + x_2}{2}, \frac{y_1 + y_2}{2} \right) \rightarrow (x_1, y_1) = (9, -6)$ and $(x_2, y_2) = (3, 8)$ Midpoint $= \left(\frac{9+3}{2}, \frac{-6+8}{2} \right) \rightarrow \left(\frac{12}{2}, \frac{2}{2} \right) \rightarrow M(6, 1)$.

Chapter 2:

Percents and Exponents

 Mathematical concepts covered:

- ⦿ Proportional Ratios
- ⦿ Similarity and Ratios
- ⦿ Percent Problems
- ⦿ Percent of Increase and Decrease
- ⦿ Discount, Tax and Tip
- ⦿ Simple Interest
- ⦿ Multiplication Property of Exponents
- ⦿ Division Property of Exponents
- ⦿ Powers of Products and Quotients
- ⦿ Zero and Negative Exponents
- ⦿ Negative Exponents and Negative Bases

Proportional Ratios

When two ratios represent the same relationship, they are considered proportional.

Proportions indicate that two ratios are equal, and they can be expressed in two formats:

$\frac{a}{b} = \frac{c}{d}$ or $(a : b = c : d)$

The proportion $\frac{a}{b} = \frac{c}{d}$ can also be written as $a \times d = c \times b$.

Examples:

1) Solve this proportion for x. $\frac{3}{5} = \frac{9}{x}$

   Use cross multiplication: $\frac{3}{5} = \frac{9}{x} \rightarrow 3 \times x = 9 \times 5 \rightarrow 3x = 45$.

   Divide both sides by 3 to find x: $x = \frac{45}{3} \rightarrow x = 15$.

2) If a box contains red and blue balls in ratio of $4 : 3$ red to blue, how many red balls are there if 18 blue balls are in the box?

   Solution: Write a proportion and solve. $\frac{4}{3} = \frac{x}{18}$

   Use cross multiplication: $4 \times 18 = 3 \times x \rightarrow 72 = 3x$.

   Divide to find x: $x = \frac{72}{3} \rightarrow x = 24$.

   There are 24 red balls in the box.

3) Solve this proportion for x. $\frac{3}{5} = \frac{15}{x}$

   Solution: Use cross multiplication: $\frac{3}{5} = \frac{15}{x} \rightarrow 3 \times x = 5 \times 15 \rightarrow 5x = 45$.

   Divide both sides by 5 to find x: $x = \frac{45}{5} \rightarrow x = 9$.

4) Solve this proportion for x. $\frac{6}{7} = \frac{36}{x}$

   Solution: Use cross multiplication: $\frac{6}{7} = \frac{36}{x} \rightarrow 6 \times x = 7 \times 36 \rightarrow 6x = 252$

   Divide to find x: $x = \frac{252}{6} \rightarrow x = 42$.

Similarity and Ratios

If two figures possess identical shapes, they are considered similar.

Additionally, two or more figures are deemed similar if their corresponding angles are equal, and their corresponding sides are in proportion.

Examples:

1) The following triangles are similar. What is the value of the unknown side?

   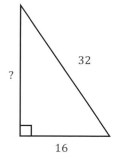

   Solution: Find the corresponding sides and write a proportion. $\frac{16}{32} = \frac{12}{x}$.

   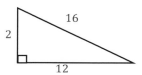

   Now, use the cross product to solve for x:

   $\frac{16}{32} = \frac{12}{x} \rightarrow 16 \times x = 32 \times 12 \rightarrow 16x = 384$.

   Divide both sides by 8. Then:

   $16x = 384 \rightarrow x = \frac{384}{16} \rightarrow x = 24$.

   The missing side is 24.

2) The two rectangles are similar. The first is $8\,feet$ wide and $32\,feet$ long. The second is $12\,feet$ wide. What is the length of the second rectangle?

   Solution: Let's put x for the length of the second rectangle. Since the two rectangles are similar, their corresponding sides are in proportion. Write a proportion and solve for the missing number.

   $\frac{8}{12} = \frac{32}{x} \rightarrow 8x = 12 \times 32 \rightarrow 8x = 384 \rightarrow x = \frac{384}{8} = 48$

   The length of the second rectangle is 48 feet.

Percent Problems

Percent is defined as the ratio of a number to 100, consistently having 100 as its denominator. The symbol used to represent percent is "%".

Percent signifies "per 100", meaning that 20% is equivalent to $\frac{20}{100}$.

When dealing with percent problems, we typically aim to find either the base, the part, or the percent.

The following equations can be utilized to determine the missing component in a percent problem:

- **Base = Part ÷ Percent**

- **Part = Percent × Base**

- **Percent = Part ÷ Base**

Examples:

1) The price of a shirt increases from $35 to $42. What is the percentage increase?

    Use this formula:

    $$\text{Percentage Increase} = \left(\frac{(New\ Value\ -\ Old\ Value)}{Old\ Value} \right) \times 100\%.$$

    Then: $\frac{42-35}{35} \times 100 = 20$. The percentage increase is 20%.

    It means that the price of the shirt increased by 20%.

2) the price of a laptop decreases from $1,000 to $800. What is the percentage decrease?

    Use this formula:

    $$Percent\ of\ change = \frac{new\ number - original\ number}{original\ number} \times 100.$$

    Then: $\frac{800-1,000}{1,000} \times 100 = \frac{-200}{10} = -20$.

    The percentage decrease is 20. (The negative sign means percentage decrease.)

    Therefore, the price of the laptop decreased by 20%.

Percent of Increase and Decrease

The concept of percent of change refers to the measurement of the extent of increase or decrease over time.

To calculate the percentage of increase or decrease, you can follow these steps:

1. *New Number – Original Number,*

2. *(The result ÷ Original Number) × 100*

3. Multiply the quotient by 100.

Alternatively, you can use the formula:

$$\text{percent of change} = \frac{new\ number - original\ number}{original\ number} \times 100.$$

It's important to note that if the resulting value is negative, it indicates a percentage decrease. Conversely, a positive value signifies a percentage increase.

Examples:

1) The price of a shirt increases from $45 to $54. What is the percentage increase?

   First, find the difference: $54 - 45 = 9$. Then, calculate the percentage increase: $(9 \div 45) \times 100 = \frac{1}{5} \times 100 = 20$. The percentage increase is 20%.

   It means that the price of the shirt increased by 20%.

2) The price of a table decreased from $70 to $55. What is the percentage of decrease?

   Percent of change= $\frac{new\ number - original\ number}{original\ number} \times 100.$

   Then: Percent of decrease $= \frac{55-70}{70} \times 100 = \frac{-15}{70} \times 100 = -21.433$. The percentage of decrease is approximately 21.43%. It means that the price of the table decreased by approximately 21.43%.

Discount, Tax and Tip

To calculate the discount, you can multiply the regular price by the discount rate.

To determine the selling price, *Original price – discount.*

To calculate the tax, multiply the tax rate by the taxable amount, which can include income, property value, and other applicable factors.

To calculate the tip, multiply the rate by the selling price.

Examples:

1) Sophia purchased a new computer for a price of $820 at the Apple Store. What is the total amount her credit card is charged if the sales tax is 5%?

   The taxable amount is $820, and the tax rate is 5%. Then:

   Tax = 0.05 × 820 = 41.

   Final price = Selling price + Tax.

   Final price = $820 + $41 = $861.

2) Nicole and her friends went out to eat at a restaurant. If their bill was $60.00 and they gave their server a 15% tip, how much did they pay altogether?

   First, find the tip. To find the tip, multiply the rate to the bill amount.

   $Tip = 60 \times 0.15 = 9.$

   The final price is: $60 + $9 = $69.

3) With an 30% discount, Mia saved $70 on a dress. What was the original price of the dress?

   let x be the original price of the dress. Then: 30% of $x = 70$.

   Write an equation and solve for x:

   $0.30 \times x = 70 \rightarrow x = \frac{70}{0.30} = 210.$

   The original price of the dress was $210.

Simple Interest

Simple Interest is the cost incurred for borrowing money or the earnings obtained from lending it.

It is calculated based on the initial amount, known as the principal.

To solve a simple interest problem, you can use the following formula:

$$Interest = principal \times rate \times time\ (I = p \times r \times t = prt)$$

Examples:

1) Find the simple interest for a $500 investment at 4% for 2 years.

   Using the interest formula:

   $I = prt$ ($P = \$500, r = 4\% = \frac{4}{100} = 0.05$ and $t = 2$).

   Then: $I = 500 \times 0.04 \times 2 = \$40$.

2) Find the simple interest for $2,000 at 6% for 4 years.

   Solution: Using the interest formula:

   $I = prt$ ($P = \$2,000, r = 6\% = \frac{6}{100} = 0.06$ and $t = 4$).

   Then: $I = 2,000 \times 0.06 \times 4 = \$480$.

3) Samantha received a personal loan to cover her expenses. What is the interest on the loan if she borrowed $7,000 at 3.5% for 8 years?

   Solution: Using the interest formula:

   $I = prt.$ ($P = \$7,000, r = 3.5\% = 0.035$ and $t = 8$).

   Then: $I = 7,000 \times 0.035 \times 8 = \$1,960$

4) Mary invested $2,500 in a savings account that earned an annual interest rate of 4.2% for 2 years. What is the interest she earned?

   Solution: Using the interest formula:

   $I = prt.$ ($P = \$2,500, r = 4.2\% = 0.042$ and $t = 2$

   Then: $I = 2,0500 \times 0.042 \times 0.2 = \$210$.

Multiplication Property of Exponents

Exponents represent a convenient method to express the repeated multiplication of a number by itself. For example, instead of 3×3, we can write 3^3. For $2 \times 2 \times 2 \times 2$, we can write 2^4.

In algebra, a variable is a symbolic representation, usually a letter, that stands in for an unspecified number. The most frequently employed letters as variables are x, y, z, a, b, c, m, and n.

Exponent's rules:

- $x^a \times x^b = x^{a+b}$
- $\dfrac{x^a}{x^b} = x^{a-b}$
- $(x^a)^b = x^{a \times b}$
- $(xy)^a = x^a \times y^a$
- $\left(\dfrac{a}{b}\right)^c = \dfrac{a^c}{b^c}$

Examples:

1) Multiply. $3x^3 \times 4x^5$

    Solution: Use Exponent's rules: $x^a \times x^b = x^{a+b} \rightarrow x^3 \times x^5 = x^{3+5} = x^8$.
    Then: $3x^3 \times 4x^5 = 12x^8$.

2) Example 2: Simplify. $(x^3 y^4)^2$

    Solution: Use Exponent's rules: $(x^a)^b = x^{a \times b}$.
    Then: $(x^3 y^4)^2 = x^{3 \times 2} y^{4 \times 2} = x^6 y^8$.

3) Example 3: Multiply. $6x^7 \times 7x^6$

    Solution: Use Exponent's rules: $x^a \times x^b = x^{a+b} \rightarrow x^7 \times x^6 = x^{7+6} = x^{13}$.
    Then: $6x^7 \times 7x^6 = 42x^{13}$.

4) Example 4: Simplify. $(x^4 y^6)^2$

    Solution: Use Exponent's rules: $(x^a)^b = x^{a \times b}$.
    Then: $(x^4 y^6)^2 = x^{4 \times 2} y^{6 \times 2} = x^8 y^{12}$.

Division Property of Exponents

For division of exponents use following formulas:

- $\dfrac{x^a}{x^b} = x^{a-b}$ $(x \neq 0)$

- $\dfrac{x^a}{x^b} = \dfrac{1}{x^{b-a}}$ $(x \neq 0)$

- $\dfrac{1}{x^b} = x^{-b}$

Examples:

1) Simplify $\dfrac{30x^8}{5x^6}$.

    Use Exponent's rules: $\dfrac{x^a}{x^b} = x^{a-b} \rightarrow \dfrac{x^8}{x^6} = x^{8-6} = x^2$. Then: $\dfrac{30x^8}{5x^6} = 6x^2$.

2) Simplify $\dfrac{18x^4y}{3xy^2}$.

    First, cancel the common factor: $3 \rightarrow \dfrac{18x^4y}{3xy^2} = \dfrac{6x^4y}{xy^2}$.

    Use Exponent's rules:

    $\dfrac{x^a}{x^b} = x^{a-b} \rightarrow \dfrac{x^4}{x} = x^{4-1} = x^3$ and $\dfrac{x^a}{x^b} = \dfrac{1}{x^{b-a}} \rightarrow \dfrac{y}{y^2} = \dfrac{1}{y^{2-1}} = \dfrac{1}{y}$. Then: $\dfrac{18x^4y}{3xy^2} = \dfrac{6x^3}{y}$.

3) Simplify $\dfrac{9x^5y^3}{27x^4y}$.

    Solution: First, cancel the common factor: $9 \rightarrow \dfrac{9x^5y^3}{27x^4y} = \dfrac{x^5y^3}{3x^4y}$

    Use Exponent's rules:

    $\dfrac{x^a}{x^b} = x^{a-b} \rightarrow \dfrac{x^5}{x^4} = x^{5-4} = x$ and $\dfrac{y^3}{y} = y^2$. Then: $\dfrac{9x^5y^3}{27x^4y} = \dfrac{xy^2}{3}$.

4) Simplify $\dfrac{10x^4y}{50x^3y^4}$.

    First cancel the common factor: $10 \rightarrow \dfrac{10x^4y}{50x^3y^4} = \dfrac{x^4y}{5x^3y^4}$.

    Use Exponent's rules: $\dfrac{x^a}{x^b} = x^{a-b} \rightarrow \dfrac{x^4}{x^3} = x^{4-3} = x$ and $\dfrac{y}{y^4} = \dfrac{y}{y^{4-1}} = \dfrac{1}{y^3}$.

    Then: $\dfrac{10x^4y}{50x^3y^4} = \dfrac{x}{5y^3}$.

Powers of Products and Quotients

For any nonzero numbers a and b and any integer x:

- $(ab)^x = a^x \times b^x$

- $\left(\dfrac{a}{b}\right)^c = \dfrac{a^c}{b^c}$

Examples:

1) Simplify $(4x^2y^3)^3$.

   Solution: Use Exponent's rules: $(x^a)^b = x^{a \times b}$.

   $(4x^2y^3)^3 = (4)^3(x^2)^3(y^3)^3 = 64x^{2\times3}y^{3\times3} = 64x^6y^9$.

2) Simplify $\left(\dfrac{3x^2}{2x}\right)^3$.

   First, cancel the common factor: $x \to \left(\dfrac{3x^2}{2x}\right)^3 = \left(\dfrac{3x}{2}\right)^3$.

   Use Exponent's rules: $\left(\dfrac{a}{b}\right)^c = \dfrac{a^c}{b^c}$, Then:

   $\left(\dfrac{3x}{2}\right)^3 = \dfrac{(3x)^3}{(2)^3} = \dfrac{27x^3}{8}$.

3) Simplify $(7x^3y^2)^2$.

   Use Exponent's rules: $(x^a)^b = x^{a \times b}$.

   $(7x^3y^2)^2 = (7)^2(x^3)^2(y^2)^2 = 49x^{3\times2}y^{2\times2} = 49x^6y^4$.

4) Simplify $\left(\dfrac{6x}{5x^2}\right)^3$.

   First, cancel the common factor: $x \to \left(\dfrac{6x}{5x^2}\right)^3 = \left(\dfrac{6}{5x}\right)^3$.

   Use Exponent's rules: $\left(\dfrac{a}{b}\right)^c = \dfrac{a^c}{b^c}$.

   Then: $\left(\dfrac{6}{5x}\right)^3 = \dfrac{6^3}{(5x)^{23}} = \dfrac{216}{125x^3}$.

5) Simplify $(-5x^2y^4)^3$.

   Use Exponent's rules: $(x^a)^b = x^{a \times b}$.

   $(-5x^2y^4)^3 = (-5)^3(x^3)^3(y^5)^3 = -125x^{2\times3}y^{4\times3} = -125x^6y^{12}$.

Zero and Negative Exponents

The Rule of Zero Exponents: If any non-zero number is raised to the power of zero, the answers is 1 ($a^0 = 1$). For instance, $(5xy)^0 = 1$.

- Note that zero itself is an exception to this rule: $0^0 = 0$

The Negative Exponent Rule: Regardless of whether the base is positive or negative, a negative exponent indicates that you should take the reciprocal of the base. In other words: $a^{-n} = \frac{1}{a^n}$

For instance, "x^{-3}" (read as "x to the power of negative three") simply means $\frac{1}{x^3}$.

Examples:

1) Evaluate $\left(\frac{6}{8}\right)^{-2}$.

   Use negative exponent's rule: $\left(\frac{x^a}{x^b}\right)^{-2} = \left(\frac{x^b}{x^a}\right)^2 \rightarrow \left(\frac{6}{8}\right)^{-2} = \left(\frac{8}{6}\right)^2$.

   Then: $\left(\frac{8}{6}\right)^2 = \frac{8^2}{6^2} = \frac{64}{36} = \frac{16}{9}$.

2) Evaluate $\left(\frac{2}{3}\right)^{-4}$.

   Use negative exponent's rule:

   $\left(\frac{x^a}{x^b}\right)^{-4} = \left(\frac{x^b}{x^a}\right)^4 \rightarrow \left(\frac{2}{3}\right)^{-4} = \left(\frac{3}{2}\right)^4$; Then: $\left(\frac{3}{2}\right)^4 = \frac{3^4}{2^4} = \frac{81}{16}$.

3) Evaluate $\left(\frac{x}{y}\right)^0$.

   Use zero-exponent Rule: $x^0 = 1$.

   Then: $\left(\frac{x}{y}\right)^0 = 1$.

4) Evaluate $\left(\frac{5}{9}\right)^{-1}$.

   Use negative exponent's rule:

   $\left(\frac{x^a}{x^b}\right)^{-1} = \left(\frac{x^b}{x^a}\right)^1 \rightarrow \left(\frac{5}{9}\right)^{-1} = \left(\frac{9}{5}\right)^1 = \frac{9}{5}$.

Negative Exponents and Negative Bases

When a negative number is raised to a power, the sign of the result depends on whether the exponent is even or odd. If you raise a negative number to an odd power, the result will be negative. If you raise it to an even power, the result will be positive. For instance:

$[(-2)^3 = -8]; [(-2)^2 = 4]$

If you have a negative base with a negative exponent: $(-a)^{-n} = \frac{1}{(-a)^n}$

So, the key things to remember:

- A negative exponent means takes the reciprocal.

- A negative base raised to an odd power will yield a negative number, whereas a negative base raised to an even power will yield a positive number.

Parentheses play an important role! -4^{-2} is not the same as $(-4)^{-2}$:

$-4^{-2} = -\frac{1}{4^2}$ and $(-4)^{-2} = +\frac{1}{4^2}$

Examples:

1) Simplify $(-2)^{-3}$.

   Use negative exponent's rule: $(-a)^{-n} = \frac{1}{(-a)^n} \rightarrow (-2)^{-3} = \left(\frac{1}{-2}\right)^3$

   Now use exponent's rule: $\left(\frac{a}{b}\right)^c = \frac{a^c}{b^c} \rightarrow = \frac{1}{(-2)^3} = \frac{1}{-8} = -\frac{1}{8}$.

2) Simplify. $\left(-\frac{6m}{3n}\right)^{-4}$.

   Use negative exponent's rule: $(-a)^{-n} = \frac{1}{(-a)^n} \rightarrow \left(-\frac{6m}{3n}\right)^{-4} = \left(-\frac{3n}{6m}\right)^4$.

   Now use exponent's rule:

   $\left(\frac{a}{b}\right)^c = \frac{a^c}{b^c} \rightarrow = \left(-\frac{3n}{6m}\right)^4$ Simplify by 3: $\left(-\frac{n}{2m}\right)^4 = \frac{n^4}{2^4 m^4}$.

   Then: $\frac{n^4}{2^4 m^4} = \frac{n^4}{16m^4}$

Chapter 3: Equations and System of Equations

 Mathematical concepts covered:

- Translate a Phrase into an Algebraic Statement
- Simplifying Variable Expressions
- Evaluating One Variable
- Evaluating Two Variables
- One–Step Equations
- Multi–Step Equations
- Rearrange Multi-Variable Equations
- Solutions of Linear Equation
- Solve Linear Equations' Word Problems
- System of Equations
- Write a System of Equations Given a Graph
- Systems of Equations Word Problems

Translate a Phrase into an Algebraic Statement

Translating key words and phrases into algebraic expressions:

- ➢ Addition: plus, more than, the sum of, Increased, etc.

- ➢ Subtraction: minus, less than, decreased by, Difference between, etc.

- ➢ Multiplication: times, product, multiplied, Times as much as, etc.

- ➢ Division: quotient, divided, ratio of, Split into, etc.

Examples:

Translate each phrase into an algebraic statement.

1) 12 times more than 8 and x.

   Sum of 8 and x: $8 + x$. Times means multiplication.

   Then: $12 \times (8 + x) = 12(8 + x)$.

2) 4 more than a number is 36.

   "More than" means plus. "a number" is x.

   Then: $4 + x = 36$.

3) 11 times the sum of 7 and x.

   Sum of 7 and x: $7 + x$. Times means multiplication. Then: $11 \times (7 + x)$.

4) three more than a number is 21.

   More than mean plus a number $+x$.

   Then: $3 + x = 21$.

5) 10 times the sum of 7 and x.

   Sum of 2 and x: $7 + x$. Times means multiplication. And $10 \times (7 + x)$.

Simplifying Variable Expressions

In the field of algebra, we utilize variables, which are essentially symbols, most commonly letters like x, y, z, a, b, c, m, and n, as placeholders for numerical values.

An algebraic expression is a combination of variables, numbers, and at least one arithmetic operation, such as addition, subtraction, multiplication, or division.

When simplifying algebraic expressions, we often combine "like terms," which are terms with the same variables raised to the same power.

For instance, in the expression $4x + 3y + 2x$, $4x$ and $2x$ are like terms and can be combined to give $6x$, simplifying the expression to $6x + 3y$.

Examples:

1) Simplify. $(5x + 3x + 7)$.

   Solution: The three terms in this expression are $5x$, $3x$, and 7. Out of these, $5x$ and $3x$ are "like" terms. Combine the like terms. $5x + 3x = 8x$.

   Then: $(5x + 3x + 7) = 8x + 7$.

   (Remember you cannot combine variables and numbers.)

2) Simplify $-3x^2 - 4x + 5x^2 - 10$.

   Solution: Combine "like" terms: $-3x^2 + 5x^2 = 2x^2$.

   Then: $-3x^2 - 4x + 5x^2 - 10 = 2x^2 - 4x - 10$.

3) Simplify $(-9 + 7x^2 + 2x^2 + 8x)$.

   Solution: Combine "like" terms: $7x^2 + 2x^2 = 9x^2$.

   Then: $(-9 + 7x^2 + 2x^2 + 8x) = 9x^2 + 8x - 9$.

4) Simplify $-10x + 6x^2 - 3x + 9x^2$.

   Solution: Combine "like" terms: $-10x - 3x = -13x$, and $6x^2 + 9x^2 = 15x^2$.

   Then: $-10x + 6x^2 - 3x + 9x^2 = -13x + 15x^2$.

Evaluating One Variable

It generally refers to determining the value of an expression when given a value for the variable it contains. To evaluate expressions with a single variable, identify the variable in the expression and replace it with a given number. Then, execute the mathematical operations appear in the expression.

Examples:

1) Evaluate this expression for $x = 3$: $5 + 4x$.

   First, substitute 3 for x.

   Then: $5 + 4x = 5 + 4(3)$.

   Now, use order of operation to find the answer:

   $5 + 4(3) = 5 + 12 = 17$.

2) Evaluate this expression for $x = -2$: $6x - 10$.

   First, substitute -2 for x.

   Then: $6x - 10 = 6(-2) - 10$.

   Now, use order of operation to find the answer:

   $6(-2) - 10 = -12 - 10 = -22$.

3) Find the value of this expression when $x = 5$. $(20 - 3x)$.

   First, substitute 5 for x,

   then: $20 - 3x = 20 - 3(5) = 20 - 15 = -45$.

4) Solve this expression for $x = -6$: $10 + 9x$.

   Solution: Substitute -6 for x.

   Then:

   $10 + 9x = 10 + 9(-6) = 10 - 54 = -44$.

5) Solve this expression for $x = -3$: $15 + 2x$.

   Substitute -3 for x.

   Then: $15 + 2x = 15 + 2(5 - 3) = 15 - 6 = -9$

Evaluating Two Variables

To compute the value of an algebraic expression, assign a specific number to each variable present in it.

The process of evaluating an algebraic expression entail substituting variables in the expression with concrete numerical values to derive a singular numerical output as the final answer. This can be done by following the steps:

- Replace the variables in the expression with the provided numerical values.

- Cut down the expression by executing the necessary mathematical operations (such as addition, subtraction, multiplication, division, or exponentiation) in the sequence prescribed by mathematical principles.

- Keep reducing the expression until you are left with a singular numerical value as the concluding answer.

Examples:

1) Evaluate this expression for a $= 3$ and $b = -2$: $(5a - 2b)$.
   First, substitute 3 for a, and -2 for b. Then: $5a - 2b = 5(3) - 2(-2)$.
   Now, use order of operation to find the answer: $5(3) - 2(-2) = 15 + 4 = 19$.

2) Evaluate this expression for $x = -3$ and $y = 3$: $(2x + 7y)$.
   Substitute -3 for x, and 3 for y.
   Then: $2x + 7y = 2(-3) + 7(3) = -6 + 21 = 15$.

3) Find the value of this expression $3(7a - 6b)$, when $a = -2$ and $b = 3$.
   Substitute -2 for a, and 3 for b.
   Then: $3(7a - 6b) = 3\big(7(-2) - 6(3)\big) = 3(-14 - 18) = 3(-32) = -96$.

4) Evaluate this expression. $-8x - 3y$, $x = -1, y = -2$
   Solution: Substitute -1 for a, and -2 for b.
   Then: $-8x - 3 == -8(-1) - 3(-2) = 8 + 6 = 14$

One–Step Equations

One-step equations are algebraic equations that require only one operation (addition, subtraction, multiplication, or division) to solve for the variable.

In an equation, the expressions on either side of the equals sign are equal in value. For example, in the equation $ax = b$, the value of ax is equivalent to the value of b.

Solving an equation involves determining the values of its variables.

For each type of operation, the key is to perform the inverse or opposite operation to isolate the variable on one side of the equation. The inverse operations to consider are:

- Addition is the inverse of subtraction and vice versa.

- Multiplication is the inverse of division and vice versa.

Examples:

1) Solve this equation for x: $5x = 20 \rightarrow x = ?$
   Here, the operation is multiplication (Variable x is multiplied by 5) and its inverse operation is division. To solve this equation, divide both sides of equation by 5:
   $5x = 20 \rightarrow \frac{5x}{5} = \frac{20}{5} \rightarrow x = 4.$

2) Solve this equation: $x + 7 = 0 \rightarrow x = ?$
   In this equation, 7 is added to the variable x. The inverse operation of addition is subtraction. To solve this equation, subtract 7 from both sides of the equation:
   $x + 7 - 7 = 0 - 7 \rightarrow x = -7.$

3) Solve this equation for x. $x - 15 = 0$
   In this equation, 15 is subtracted from x. The inverse operation of subtraction is addition. To solve the equation, add 15 to both sides of the equation:
   $x - 15 + 15 = 0 + 15 \rightarrow x = 15.$

Multi–Step Equations

A multi-step equation involves more than one operation to solve. Solving such equations may require a combination of addition, subtraction, multiplication, division, distribution, and combining like terms.

Here's how to solve a multi-step equation:

- ✓ Distribute any numbers (if necessary).
- ✓ Combine like terms on each side of the equation. This means, collect terms that have the same variable and same power together.
- ✓ Isolate the variable using inverse operations.
- ✓ It's always a good idea to double-check your work. Substituting the solution back into the original equation and confirming that both sides of the equation are equal.

Examples:

1) Solve this equation for x. $2(x - 3) + 5 = 3x - 1$

   Step 1: Distribute: $2x - 6 + 5 = 3x - 1$

   Step 2: Combine like terms on each side: $2x - 1 = 3x - 1$

   Step 3: Isolate the variable:

   Subtract $2x$ from both sides: $-1 = x - 1$

   Now, add 1 to both sides to solve for (x): $x = 0$

   So, the solution is $(x = 0)$.

   Check the solution by substituting $x = 0$ into the original equation:

   $2(0 - 3) + 5 = 3(0) - 1 \rightarrow -6 + 5 = -1 \rightarrow -1 = -1$. The solution is correct.

2) Solve this equation for y. $3y + 5 = 25 - y$

   First, move variables to one side by adding y to both sides. Then:

   $3y + 5 + y = 25 - y + y$. Simplify $4y + 5 = 25$.

   Next, subtract 5 from both sides of the equation: $4y + 5 - 5 = 25 - 5$

   $\rightarrow 4y = 20 \rightarrow$ Divide both sides by 4: $\frac{4y}{4} = \frac{20}{4} \rightarrow y = 5$.

   Let's check this solution by substituting y = 5 into the original equation e:

   $3y + 5 = 25 - y \rightarrow\rightarrow 3(5) + 5 = 25 - 5 \rightarrow 20 = 20$. The solution is correct.

Rearrange Multi-Variable Equations

When it comes to rearranging equations involving multiple variables:

- ✓ Identify the dependent variable first.

- ✓ Try to get the dependent variable by itself on one side of the equation.

- ✓ Reverse the operations on both sides of the equation to express the dependent variable solely in terms of the other variables.

Examples:

1) Express x as the subject of the equation: $2x - 5 = z$.

   To isolate x on one side of the equation, first add 5 to both sides as follows:

   $2x - 5 + 5 = z + 5 \rightarrow 2x = z + 5$.

   Then divide both sides of the equation by 2: $\frac{2x}{2} = \frac{(z+5)}{2} \rightarrow x = \frac{(z+5)}{2}$.

2) Solve for p in terms of q and r: $r + q - p = 4$.

   To solve the problem, find p. By canceling the operations on both sides, Isolate p on one side of the equation. Add p to both sides of the equation. So,

   $r + q - p + p = 4 + p \rightarrow r + q = p + 4$.

   Now, subtract 4 from both sides of the equation, then:

   $r + q - 4 = p + 4 - 4 \rightarrow r + q - 4 = p$.

   In this case, the above equation in terms of p becomes: $p = r + q - 4$

3) Solve $V = \frac{1}{4}\pi r^2 h$ for h.

   To isolate h on both sides of the equation, just multiply the sides by the expression $\frac{4}{\pi r^2}$. Therefore, $\frac{4}{\pi r^2} \times V = \frac{4}{\pi r^2}\left(\frac{1}{4}\pi r^2 h\right) \rightarrow h = \frac{4V}{\pi r^2}$.

4) Solve $y = mx + b$ for m.

   To isolate m on one side of the equation, subtract b from both sides, then divide both sides by x:

   $y - b = mx + b - b \rightarrow \frac{(y - b)}{x} = m$.

Solutions of Linear Equation

A linear equation is an equation in which the highest degree of any variable is 1. It represents a straight line on a graph.

Linear equations can have three possible outcomes:

No solution: A linear equation has no solution when solving it leads to a contradictory or false statement.

One solution: A linear equation has one solution when solving it results in a true statement for a single value of the variable.

Infinitely many solutions: A linear equation has infinitely many solutions when solving it yields a statement that is always true, regardless of the value of the variable.

Examples:

1) How many solutions does the following equation have?

$$7 - 5p = -5p$$

Solve for p: $7 - 5p = -5p \rightarrow 7 = +5p - 5p \rightarrow 7 = 0.7 = 0$ is a false statement. The linear equation has no solution because by solving the linear equation you get a false statement as an answer.

2) How many solutions does the following equation have?

$$24h = 6h + 54$$

Solve for h: $24h = 6h + 54 \rightarrow 24h - 6h = 54 \rightarrow 18h = 54 \rightarrow h = 3$. $h = 3$ is a true statement for a single value for the variable. So, the linear equation has one solution because by solving a linear equation you get a true statement for a single value for the variable.

3) How many solutions does the following equation have?

$$4n - n = 3n$$

Simplify the left side of the equation $4n - n = 3n \rightarrow 3n = 3n$. $3n = 3n$ is a statement that is always true. So, the equation has infinitely many solutions because by solving a linear equation you get a statement that is always true.

Solve Linear Equations' Word Problems

The key to solving word problems is understanding the relationships presented in the problem, identifying the unknowns, setting up equations to represent those relationships, and then solving for the unknowns. Follow these steps:

1. Carefully read the entire problem and determine what you are being asked to find.

2. Look for keywords or information in the problem that can be represented by variables. Assign variables to the unknown quantities in the problem.

3. Utilize the information given in the problem to construct an algebraic equation. Translate the problem into a mathematical representation, considering the relationships and conditions stated.

4. Solve the one-step or two-step equation that you have obtained. Once you have solved the linear equation, you will have the value of the variable that satisfies the equation and solves the problem.

Example:

✎ Larry is in a chocolate shop and is going to buy some chocolates for his friends. He chooses 4 chocolates with a flower design and in addition, he also chooses some packs of three chocolates. If the total number of chocolates he has bought is 28, write an equation that you can use to find p, the number of packs of three chocolates. How many packs of three chocolates has Larry bought?

Let's set up the equation to find p, the number of packs of three chocolates:

Larry has 4 chocolates accounted. The remaining chocolates that he chooses are in packs of three. Let's say p represents the number of packs of three chocolates. Each pack of three chocolates contains 3 chocolates, so the number of chocolates in the packs is 3p.

The total number of chocolates Larry has bought is given as 34. So, we can write the equation: $4 + 3p = 34$.

Now, we can solve this equation to find the value of p. By subtracting 4 from both sides of the equation: $3p + 4 - 4 = 34 - 4 \rightarrow 3p = 30$

Then, divide both sides by 3: $p = \frac{30}{3} \rightarrow p = 10$

Larry has bought 10 packs of three chocolates.

System of Equations

A system of equations contains two equations with two variables. For the system of equations: $x - y = 1, x + y = 5$.

The **elimination method** is the easiest way to solve a system of equations. It utilizes the addition property of equality, which allows us to add the same value to each side of an equation.

For the first equation above, you can add $x + y$ to the left side and 5 to the right side of the first equation: $(x - y) + (x + y) = 1 + 5$. Simplifying the equation: $2x = 6$.

Now, we can solve for x by dividing both sides of the equation by 2: $\frac{2x}{2} = \frac{6}{2}$, which gives us $x = 3$.

Substituting $x = 3$ into the first equation $(x - y = 1)$, we get: $3 - y = 1$.

Solving this equation, we find that $y = 2$.

Therefore, the solution to the system of equations is $x = 3$ and $y = 2$.

Examples:

1) What is the value of $x + y$ in this system of equations? $\begin{cases} 2x + 4y = 12 \\ 4x - 2y = -16 \end{cases}$

   Solving a System of Equations by Elimination: multiply the first equation by (-2), then add it to the second equation.

   $$\begin{cases} -2(2x + 4y = 12) \\ 4x - 2y = -16 \end{cases} \rightarrow \begin{cases} -4x - 8y = -24 \\ 4x - 2y = -16 \end{cases} \rightarrow -10y = -40 \rightarrow y = 4$$

   Plug in the value of y into one of the equations and solve for x.

   $2x + 4(4) = 12 \rightarrow 2x + 16 = 12 \rightarrow 2x = 12 - 16 \rightarrow 2x = -4 \rightarrow x = -2$.

   Thus, $x + y = -2 + 4 = 2$.

2) What is the value of $x - y$ in this system of equations? $\begin{cases} 2x - 6y = -1 \\ -4x + 3y = -1 \end{cases}$

   Using elimination method: multiply the second equation by (2), then add it to the first equation. $\begin{cases} 2x - 6y = -1 \\ 2(-4x + 3y = -1) \end{cases} \rightarrow \begin{cases} 2x - 6y = -1 \\ -8x - 6y = -2 \end{cases} \rightarrow -6x = -3 \rightarrow x = \frac{1}{2}$

   Plug in the value of x into one of the equations and solve for y.

   $2\left(\frac{1}{2}\right) - 6y = -1 \rightarrow 1 - 6y = -1 \rightarrow -6y = -1 - 1 \rightarrow y = \frac{-2}{-6} = \frac{1}{3}$.

   Thus, $x - y = \frac{1}{2} - \frac{1}{3} = \frac{3-2}{6} = \frac{1}{6}$.

Write a System of Equations Given a Graph

A system of equations consists of 2 or more equations and tries to find common solutions to the equations. In the case of a system of linear equations, the same set of variables can satisfy all the equations.

To write a system of equations based on a graph, follow these steps:

1. Examine each line in the graph. Each line represents a linear equation in the system.

2. Determine the slope (m) and y-intercept (b) of the first line:

    To find the slope, you can use any two points on the line and apply the slope formula: $m = \frac{(change\ in\ y)}{(change\ in\ x)}$. To determine the y-intercept, observe the point at which the line crosses the $y - axis$.

3. Use the values of the slope and y-intercept to construct the equation of the first line in slope-intercept form.

4. Repeat the same process to find the equation of the second line using its slope and $y - intercept$.

Example:

✎ Write a system of equations for the following graph.

First, look at the green line: to find the slope, you can use any two points on the line ($(0,4)$ and $(-8,0)$)and plug in the slope equation:

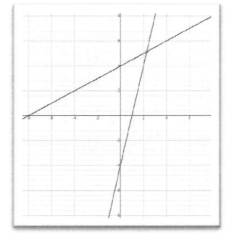

$m = \frac{change\ in\ y}{change\ in\ x} = \frac{0-4}{-8-0} = \frac{-4}{-8} = \frac{1}{2}$.

The green line crosses the $y-$axis at $(0,4)$, so the $y-$intercept is $b = 4$.

The equation of the blue line: $y = \frac{1}{2}x + 4$.

You can find the green line's equation in the same way. Use the points $(0,-4)$ and $(2,4)$: $\frac{4-(-4)}{2-0} = 4$. The blue line crosses the $y-$axis at $(0,-4)$, so the $y-$intercept is $b = -4$. The equation of the blue line: $y = 4x - 4$

Therefore, the graph shows the following system of equations: $\begin{cases} y = \frac{1}{2}x + 4 \\ y = 4x - 4 \end{cases}$

Systems of Equations Word Problems

1. Analyze the word problem and identify the key information that will help formulate two equations.
2. Define two variables, usually denoted as x and y, to represent the unknown quantities in the problem.
3. Write two equations using the variables, based on the given information from the problem. These equations should accurately represent the relationship between the variables.
4. Choose a suitable method that aligns best with the given equations and the problem at hand. Common methods include elimination, substitution, or graphing. Select the method.
5. Solve the system of equations using the chosen method. Find the values of x and y that satisfy both equations simultaneously.
6. Check your solutions by substituting the values of x and y back into the original equations. Ensure that the solutions satisfy both equations and produce true statements.
7. Finally, answer the questions posed in the real-world problem using the obtained values of x and y. Interpret the solutions in the context of the problem and provide a meaningful answer.

Example:

✎ Tickets to a concert cost \$12 for adults and \$8 for students. A group of friends purchased a total of 25 tickets for \$260. How many adult tickets did they buy?

Let x: be the number of adult tickets; y: the number of student tickets.

There are 25 tickets. Then: $x + y = 25$. The cost of adults' tickets is \$8 and for students it is \$5, and the total cost is \$260. So, $8x + 12y = 260$. Now, we have a system of equations: $\begin{cases} x + y = 25 \\ 12x + 8y = 260 \end{cases}$. Multiply the first equation by -8 and add it to the second equation: $-8(x + y = 25) = -8x - 8y = -200$.

$8x + 12y + (-8x - 8y) = 260 - 200 \rightarrow 4x = 60 \rightarrow x = 15$

$x + y = 25 \rightarrow 15 + y = 25 \rightarrow y = 10$.

There are 15 adult tickets and 10 student tickets. Now, check your answers by substituting solutions into the original equations.

$x + y = 25 \rightarrow 15 + 10 = 25$, $12x + 8y = 260 \rightarrow 12(15) + 8(10) = 260 \rightarrow 180 + 80 = 260$. The solutions are correct in both equations.

Chapter 4: Inequalities and System of Inequalities

 Mathematical concepts covered:

- ◉ One–Step Inequalities
- ◉ Multi–Step Inequalities
- ◉ Solve Advanced Linear Inequalities in Two-Variables
- ◉ Compound Inequalities
- ◉ Two-variable Inequalities Word Problems
- ◉ Write a Linear Inequality from a Graph
- ◉ Graph Solutions to Linear Inequalities
- ◉ Graph Solutions to Advance Linear Inequalities
- ◉ Absolute Value Inequalities
- ◉ Systems of Linear Inequalities

www.mathnotion.com

{ 49 }

One–Step Inequalities

An inequality compares two expressions using an inequality sign. Inequality signs are:

- "Less than" <, "greater than" >,
- "Less than or equal to" ≤, and "greater than or equal to" ≥.

You only need to perform one Math operation to solve the one-step inequalities.

To solve one-step inequalities, you typically need to perform a single mathematical operation. The goal is to find the inverse (opposite) operation that is being performed. When dividing or multiplying both sides of an inequality by negative numbers, it's necessary to flip the direction of the inequality sign.

Interval notation is a method used to represent the solutions of an inequality. It employs brackets and parentheses to indicate whether the endpoints are included or excluded from the solution set. For instance, consider the inequality $x > 2$. The solution set for this inequality includes all real numbers greater than 2, extending to infinity. The interval notation for this solution set would be $(2, \infty)$, indicating that x is any number greater than 2, but 2 itself is not included.

On the other hand, if the inequality is $x \geq 2$, the solution set includes 2, and the interval notation for this solution set would be $[2, \infty)$, meaning that x is any number greater than or equal to 2, including 2. It is important to note that negative infinity is represented by the symbol " $-\infty$".

Examples:

1) Solve this inequality for x. $x + 6 \geq 5$

   Solution: The inverse (opposite) operation of addition is subtraction. In this inequality, 6 is added to x. To isolate x we need to subtract 6 from both sides of the inequality.

   Then: $x + 6 \geq 5 \rightarrow x + 6 - 6 \geq 5 - 6 \rightarrow x \geq -1$.

   The solution is: $x \geq -1$ or $[-1, \infty)$

2) Solve the inequality. $x - 4 > -7$

   Solution: 4 is subtracted from x. Add 4 to both sides.

   $$x - 4 > -7 \rightarrow x - 4 + 4 > -7 + 4 \rightarrow x > -4 \text{ or } [-4, \infty)$$

Multi–Step Inequalities

To solve a multi-step inequality, follow these steps:

- Combine "like" terms on one side of the inequality.

- Bring the variables to one side of the inequality by adding or subtracting terms.

- Isolate the variable by performing necessary operations, such as multiplying or dividing both sides of the inequality.

- Simplify the equation further using the inverse (opposite) of addition or subtraction.

- Continue simplifying by using the inverse of multiplication or division.

- If you multiply or divide both sides of the inequality by negative numbers, remember to flip the direction of the inequality sign.

Examples:

1) Solve this inequality. $6x - 3 \leq 9$

   Solution: In this inequality, 3 is subtracted from $8x$. The inverse of subtraction is addition. Add 2 to both sides of the inequality: $6x - 3 + 3 \leq 9 + 3 \rightarrow 6x \leq 12$.

   Now, divide both sides by 8. Then: $6x \leq 12 \rightarrow \frac{6x}{6} \leq \frac{12}{6} \rightarrow x \leq 2$.

   The solution of this inequality is $x \leq 2$ or $(-\infty, 2]$

2) Solve this inequality. $4x + 5 < 9$

   Solution: First, subtract 9 from both sides: $4x + 5 - 5 < 9 - 5$.

   Then simplify: $4x + 5 - 5 < 9 - 4x < 4$.

   Now divide both sides by 4: $\frac{4x}{4} < \frac{4}{4} \rightarrow x < 1$ or $(-\infty, 1)$

3) Solve this inequality. $-2x + 6 \geq 10$

   Solution: First, subtract 3 from both sides: $-2x + 6 - 6 \geq 10 - 6 \rightarrow -2x \geq 4$.

   Divide both sides by -2. Remember that you need to flip the direction of inequality sign. $-2x \geq 4 \rightarrow \frac{-2x}{-2} \leq \frac{4}{-2} \rightarrow x \leq -2$ or $(-\infty, -2]$

Solve Advanced Linear Inequalities in Two-Variables

The general form of a linear inequality in two-variable has a general form of:

$$Ax + By < C,$$

Where inequality sign can be any of the following: greater than ($>$), less than ($<$), less than or equal to ($\leq$), greater than or equal to ($\geq$), or not equal to ($\neq$).

To solve a linear inequality, convert the given inequality to the general form.

Use the inverse operations to undo the inequality operations for both sides of the inequality to arrive at the general form.

To solve a linear inequality in two-variable in general form substitute different ordered pairs (x, y) into the inequality and check if the inequality holds true for each pair. All ordered pairs that produce a true statement when substituted into the inequality represent solutions.

Examples:

1) Solve the inequality $2x - 1 \geq 3y + 2x$.

    Solution: First, convert to the general form. Add 2 to both sides of the inequality.

    So, $2x - 1 + 1 \geq 3y + 2x + 1 \rightarrow 2x \geq 3y + 2x + 1$.

    Subtract $3y$ from both sides as $2x - 3y \geq 3y + 2x + 1 - 3y$

    $\rightarrow 2x - 3y \geq 2x + 1$. Also, subtract $2x$ from the sides:

    $2x - 3y \geq 2x + 1 \rightarrow 2x - 2x - 3y \geq 2x - 2x + 1 \rightarrow -3y \geq 1$.

    Divide both sides by -3, remembering to flip the direction of the inequality:

    $\frac{(-3y)}{(-3)} \leq \frac{1}{(-3)} \rightarrow y \leq \frac{-1}{3}$ The solution to this inequality is all ordered pairs in the

    form of (x, y) where $y \leq \frac{-1}{3}$. That is, $\{(x, y) \mid x \in \mathbb{R}, y \leq \frac{-1}{3}\}$.

2) Solve the inequality $y + 4 < x - 2$.

    Solution: Convert to the general form. Subtract 4 from both sides. So,

    $y + 4 - 4 < x - 2 - 4 \rightarrow y < x - 6$.

    Now, subtract y from both sides; $y < x - 6 \rightarrow y - x < -6$. The answer to this inequality is all ordered pairs in the form of (x, y) where $x > y - 6$. That is: $\{(x, y) \mid y \in R, x > y - 6\}$.

Compound Inequalities

A compound inequality consists of two or more inequalities that are connected by the words "and" or "or".

To solve compound inequalities, follow these steps:

1. Isolate the variable by performing the necessary operations, such as addition, subtraction, multiplication, or division.

2. When dividing by a negative number, flip the sign of the inequality.

3. Simplify the inequality using inverse operations.

For compound inequalities with the word "and" look for values that satisfy all the individual inequalities or the intersection of the inequalities.

For compound inequalities with the word "or" solve each inequality separately. Then, graph the solutions for each inequality. To find the solution to the compound inequality, combine the numbers that belong to each graph.

To combine the solution sets of two or more inequalities, use the union symbol "∪". For example, if we have the inequalities $x < -5$ and $x > 2$, their solution sets can be represented as $(-\infty, -5)$ and $(2, \infty)$ respectively, using interval notation. The union of these two intervals represents the combined solution set, which is $x < -5$ or $x > 2$, written as $(-\infty, -5) \cup (2, \infty)$.

Examples:

1) Solve. $10 < 2x \leq 40$

   Solution: To solve this inequality, divide all sides of the inequality by 2. This simplifies the inequality as follows: $5 < x \leq 20$ or $(5, 20]$.

2) Solve. $x - 7 < -13$ or $\frac{x}{4} > 6$

   Solution: Solve each inequality by isolating the variable:

   $x - 7 < -13 \rightarrow x - 7 + 7 < -13 + 7 \rightarrow x < -6$.

   Then: $\frac{x}{4} > 6 \rightarrow \frac{x}{4} \times 4 > 6 \times 4 \rightarrow x > 24$.

   The solution to these two inequalities is:

   $x < -6$ and $x > 24$ or $(-\infty, -6) \cup (24, \infty)$

Two-variable Inequalities Word Problems

Solving word problems involving two-variable inequalities is a bit more challenging than standard linear equations, but the approach is similar. Here's a step-by-step guide:

1) **Understand the Problem:** Carefully read the problem at least once to understand what's being asked and what information is provided.

2) **Define the Variables:** Assign variables to the unknown quantities. For two-variable problems, you will often assign variables to two distinct but related quantities.

3) **Translate into Inequalities:** Translate the given information into one or more inequalities involving the variables you've defined. This is the most challenging step. Look for keywords that indicate the relationship between quantities:

   - "Greater than" or "more than" $\rightarrow$ >
   - "At least" or "no less than" $\rightarrow$ $\geq$
   - "Less than" or "fewer than" $\rightarrow$ <
   - "At most" or "no more than" $\rightarrow$ $\leq$

4) **Solve the Inequality:** This could mean isolating the variable on one side or graphing a system of inequalities to find a feasible region. For two-variable inequalities, this might involve expressing (y) (or (x)) in terms of the other variable.

5) **Interpret the Solution:** Make sure your solution makes sense in the context of the problem.

Example:

1) A toy company produces dolls and trucks. Each doll requires 2 hours of labor, and each truck requires 3 hours. The company has at most 30 hours available for production each day. If each doll yields a profit of $5 and each truck yields a profit of $7, and they want to earn at least $100 daily, how many of each toy should they produce?

   - **Understand the Problem**: We need to determine the number of dolls and trucks to produce to meet labor hours and profit constraints.
   - **Define the Variables**:

     Let (d) = number of dolls

     Let (t) = number of trucks

- **Translate Words into Mathematical Inequalities**:

Labor constraint: 2 hours/doll and 3 hours/truck, with at most 30 hours available.

Profit goal: $5 profit/doll and $7 profit/truck, with at least $100 desired.

- **Setup the System of Inequalities**:

$[\, 2d + 3t \leq 30 \,]$ (Labor hours constraint)

$[\, 5d + 7t \geq 100 \,]$ (Profit goal)

- **Graph and Solve**:

You would graph these inequalities on a coordinate plane, with $(\,d\,)$ on the x-axis and $(\,t\,)$ on the y-axis. The feasible region (where the shaded areas of the inequalities overlap) represents combinations of dolls and trucks that meet both constraints.

- **Interpret the Solution**:

The coordinates in the feasible region represent the number of dolls and trucks the company can produce to meet their labor and profit goals. Choose the combination that best suits the company's objectives.

2) A company makes two products, A and B. They can make at most 150 products in a day. Product A takes 2 hours to make, and Product B takes 3 hours. They have at most 400 hours available. How many of each product can they make?

Let (x) be the number of Product A and (y) be the number of Product B.

From the problem:

1) $(\, x + y \leq 150 \,)$ (They can make at most 150 products)

2) $(\, 2x + 3y \leq 400 \,)$ (Time constraint)

Graph each inequality. The feasible region (the overlapping shaded area of both inequalities) will give the range of values for $(\,x\,)$ and $(\,y\,)$ that the company can make given the constraints.

From here, further analysis, such as linear programming, may be required if the company wants to optimize for profit or other metrics.

Remember, in word problems, always ensure your solutions make sense in the given context.

Write a Linear Inequality from a Graph

To write a linear inequality from a graph, follow these steps:

1. Look at the graph and determine whether the inequality line is represented by a dashed line or a solid line. If it's a dashed line, the inequality sign will be either $<$ or $>$. If it's a solid line, the inequality sign will be either $\leq$ or $\geq$.

2. Consider any two points on the inequality line. Using these two points, you can determine the equation of the inequality line.

3. Find the slope of the inequality line using the two points. You can use the slope formula: $m = \frac{(y2 - y1)}{x2 - x1}$.

4. Substitute the slope value and one of the points into the formula $y = mx + b$. In this formula, m represents the slope of the line, (x, y) is a point on the line, and b represents the y-intercept.

5. Look at the shaded region of the graph and determine whether y is less than the obtained equation or greater than the obtained equation. You can substitute a point from the shaded region into the equation to determine the sign of inequality.

Example:

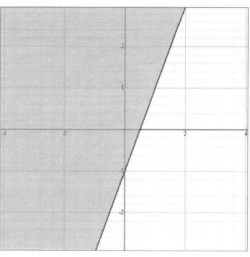

✎ Write the slope-intercept form equation of the following graph.

Solution: To write the inequality equation in slope-intercept form, you should find the y −intercept (b), and the slope (m), of the solid line. The value of b is -1 because the solid line passes through the y −axis at $(0, -1)$. Now consider 2 points on the solid line to find the slope. You can use $(0, -1)$ and $(-1, -3)$: $m = \frac{(y2-y1)}{(x2-x1)} = \frac{-3+1}{-1-0} = \frac{-2}{-1} = 2 \rightarrow$ $m = 2$. Now use the value of b and m and put them into the slope-intercept form formula: $y = mx + b \rightarrow y = 2x - 1$. Determine the symbol of inequality: you have a solid line, and the shaded part is above the line. So, the equation of the inequality is as follows: $y \geq 2x - 1$.

Graph Solutions to Linear Inequalities

An inequality is a mathematical statement that compares two expressions using an inequality sign, such as greater than (>), less than (<), greater than or equal to (≥), or less than or equal to (≤).

inequalities that you can solve using only one step are called one-step inequalities. Inequalities that you should take two steps to solve are called two-step inequalities.

To solve one-step and two-step linear inequalities for a variable, you need to use inverse operations to undo the operations and isolate the variable in the inequality. It is important to perform the same operation on both sides of the inequality to maintain its balance. When multiplying or dividing by a negative number, remember to reverse the direction of the inequality symbol.

To graph an inequality, a number is represented using a filled-in circle if it is included in the solution set. Conversely, an open circle is used to represent a number that is excluded from the solution set.

Examples:

1) Solve the following inequality and graph the solution. $m + 4 \geq 9$

    Solution: Solve for m: $m + 4 \geq 9 \rightarrow m \geq 9 - 4 \rightarrow m \geq 5$. Now graph $m \geq 5$. The inequality $m \geq 5$ means that m can be any number more than or equal to 5. m can be equal to 5, so you should use a filled-in circle located on 5. Also, m can be more than 5, so you should also draw an arrow pointing to the left:

2) Solve the following inequality and graph the solution. $-10q - 6 < 14$

    Solution: $-5q - 3 < 7$ is a two-step inequality. First, solve for q: $-10q - 6 < 14 \rightarrow -10q < 6 + 14 \rightarrow -10q < 20 \rightarrow q > -2$. Now graph $q > -2$. The inequality $q > -2$ means that q can be any number more than -2. q can't be equal to -2, so you should use an open circle located on -2. Also, q can be more than -2, so you should also draw an arrow pointing to the right:

Graph Solutions to Advance Linear Inequalities

To solve an inequality, follow these steps:

1. Use inverse operations to undo the inequality operations for both sides of the inequality. Perform the same operation on both sides to maintain the balance of the inequality.

2. When dividing or multiplying both sides of the inequality by negative numbers, remember to flip the direction of the inequality sign.

3. Continue simplifying the inequality until the variable is isolated on one side and the other components are on the other side.

To graph an inequality, use the following symbols:

- Use a filled-in circle (●) to represent a number when it is included in the solution set of the inequality.

- Use an open circle (○) to represent a number when it is excluded from the solution set of the inequality.

Examples:

1) Solve the inequality $6x + 2 \geq 6 - 2x$.

   Combine like terms: Subtract 2 from both sides $6x + 2 - 2 \geq 6 - 2x - 2 \rightarrow 6x \geq 4 - 2x$. Now, add $2x$ to the sides. So, $6x + 2x \geq 4 - 2x + 2x \rightarrow 8x \geq 4$. Finally, divide by 8 and simplify. Therefore, $8x \geq 4 \rightarrow x \geq \frac{1}{2}$.

   To graph, put a filled-in circle instead of the point $\frac{1}{2}$ on the real number axis and draw a line to positive infinity:

2) Solve the inequality Solve the inequality $\frac{2x+6}{-6} < 2x + 1$.

   Multiply both sides by -6 to eliminate the denominator. When multiplying by a negative number, remember to flip the direction of the inequality sign. $-6\left(\frac{2x+6}{-6}\right) > -6(2x+1) \rightarrow 2x + 6 > -6(2x+1) \rightarrow 2x + 6 > -12x - 6$.

   Combine like terms: $2x + 12x > -6 - 6 \rightarrow 14x > -12$. Finally, divide both sides of the inequality by 14. Therefore, $x > -\frac{12}{14} > -\frac{6}{7}$. To graph, put an open circle instead of the point $-\frac{6}{7}$ on the axis and draw a line to $+\infty$. We have:

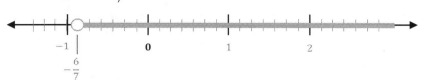

Absolute Value Inequalities

An absolute value inequality consists of an absolute value$|a|$ and a sign of inequality ($<$, $>$, $\leq$, $\geq$).

To solve an absolute value inequality, we transform it into a simple inequality by considering the direction of the inequality. Depending on the direction of the inequality, we use one of the following methods:

❖ To solve x in the inequality $|ax + b| < c$, you must solve.

$$-c < ax + b < c.$$

❖ To solve x in the inequality $|ax + b| > c$ you must solve:

$$ax + b > c \text{ and } ax + b < -c.$$

By applying these methods, we can solve absolute value inequalities by transforming them into simple inequalities that align with the given direction of the inequality.

Examples:

1) Solve. $|3x - 2| \leq 5$.

Since the inequality sign is $\leq$, rewrite the inequality to: $-5 \leq 3x - 2 \leq 5$.

Then, solve the inequality:

$$-5 + 2 < 3x < 5 + 2 \rightarrow -3 < 3x < 7$$

Now, divide each section by 3: $-3 \leq 3x \leq 7 \rightarrow \frac{-3}{3} \leq \frac{3x}{3} \leq \frac{7}{3} \rightarrow -1 \leq x \leq \frac{7}{3}$

You can also write this solution using the interval symbol: $\left[-1, \frac{7}{3}\right]$

2) Solve. $|x + 3| > 13$.

Solution: Since the inequality sign is $>$, rewrite the inequality to:

$x + 3 > 13$ and $x + 3 < -13$. Now, simplify both inequalities:

$x + 3 > 13 \rightarrow x > 10$ and $x + 3 < -13 \rightarrow x < -16$ or $(-\infty, -16) \cup (10, +\infty)$

Systems of Linear Inequalities

A system of linear inequalities is a set of two or more inequalities. Each of the inequalities is solved separately, and the common answer between these inequalities is the answer of the linear inequality system.

If you cannot mentally find the answers to the inequalities, just draw on their axis and find the common ground.

Example:

✎ Solve the following system of inequalities:

$$\begin{cases} 4x - 2y \le 6 \\ x + 2y \le 6 \\ y \ge 0 \end{cases}$$

Solution: As much as possible, we simplify each of the inequalities based on

$$y: \begin{cases} 4x - 2y \le 6 \rightarrow -2y \le -4x + 6 \rightarrow y \ge 2x - 3 \\ x + 2y \le 4 \rightarrow 2y \le -x + 4 \rightarrow y \le -\dfrac{x}{2} + 2 \\ y \ge 0 \end{cases} \rightarrow \begin{cases} y \ge 2x - 3 \\ y \le -\dfrac{x}{2} + 2 \\ y \ge 0 \end{cases}$$

Draw a graph for each inequality. The answer to the system of inequalities is the common points between the graphs:

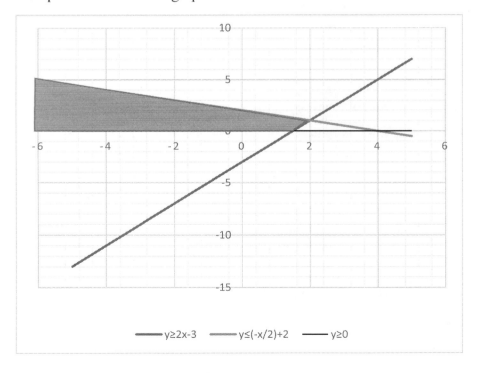

Chapter 5: linear functions

 Mathematical concepts covered:

- Finding Slope
- Writing Linear Equations
- Graph an Equation in the Standard Form
- Graphing Linear Inequalities
- Write an Equation from a Graph
- Slope-intercept Form and Point-slope Form
- Write a Point-slope Form Equation from a Graph
- Intercepts (x and y −intercept)
- Equations of Horizontal and Vertical lines
- Graph a Horizontal or Vertical line
- Graph an Equation in Point-Slope Form
- Equation of Parallel and Perpendicular Lines
- Compare Linear Function's Graph and Equations
- Graphing Absolute Value Equations
- Two-variable Linear Equations' Word Problems

Finding Slope

The slope of a line represents the rate of change and can be thought of as the "steepness" or "tilt" of the line. In a two-dimensional Cartesian coordinate system, the slope (m) of a straight line is defined as the ratio of the vertical change (rise) to the horizontal change (run) between two distinct points on the line.

Mathematically, if you have two points, $((x_1, y_1))$ and $((x_2, y_2))$, the slope (m) is calculated as: $m = \frac{y_2 - y_1}{x_2 - x_1}$

Key points about slope:

- Positive Slope: If the line rises as you move from left to right, the slope is positive.
- Negative Slope: If the line falls as you move from left to right, the slope is negative.
- Zero Slope: A horizontal line has a slope of 0 because there's no vertical change.
- Undefined Slope: A vertical line has an undefined slope because the horizontal change (denominator) is 0, leading to a division by zero.

The equation of a line is typically written as $y = mx + b$ where m is the slope and b is the $y-$intercept.

Examples:

1) Find the slope of the line through these two points A$(-2, 4)$ and B$(1, -3)$.

   Solution: Slope $= \frac{y_2 - y_1}{x_2 - x_1}$.

   Let (x_1, y_1) be A$(1, -6)$ and (x_2, y_2) be B$(3, 2)$.

   (Remember, you can choose any point for (x_1, y_1) and (x_2, y_2)).

   Then: Slope $= \frac{y_2 - y_1}{x_2 - x_1} = \frac{-3 - 4}{(1 - 2)} = \frac{-7}{3}$.

   The slope of the line through these two points is $\frac{-7}{3}$.

2) Given two points (A$(1,3)$) and (B$(3,7)$), let's find the slope.

   Using the formula: Slope $= \frac{y_2 - y_1}{x_2 - x_1}$

   $$m = \frac{7 - 3}{3 - 1} \rightarrow m = \frac{4}{2} \rightarrow m = 2$$

   So, the slope of the line passing through points A and B is 2.

Writing Linear Equations

The equation of a line in slope-intercept form: $y = mx + b$.

To write this equation, the first step is to determine the slope of the line. Next, find the y-intercept, which is the point where the line intersects the y-axis. To determine the $y - intercept$, substitute the slope (m) and the coordinates of a point (x, y) that lies on the line into the equation.

Examples:

1) What is the equation of the line that passes through $(5, -2)$ and has a slope of 7?

   Solution: The general slope-intercept form of the equation of a line is:

   $y = mx + b$,

   where m is the slope and b is the $y -$intercept.

   By substitution of the given point and given slope, we get:

   $y = mx + b \rightarrow -2 = (7)(5) + b$.

   So, $b = -2 - 35 = -37$, and the required equation of the line is: $y = 7x - 37$.

2) Write the equation of the line through two points $A(4,2)$ and $B(-1,7)$.

   Solution: First, find the slope: slope $= \frac{y_2 - y_1}{x_2 - x_1} = \frac{7-2}{-1-4} = \frac{5}{-5} = -1 \rightarrow m = -1$.

   To find the value of b, either of the points and plug in the values of x and y in the equation. The answer will be the same: $y = -x + b$. Let's check both points.

   Then: $(4,2) \rightarrow y = mx + b \rightarrow 2 = -1(4) + b \rightarrow b = 6$.

   $(-1,7) \rightarrow y = mx + b \rightarrow 7 = -1(-1) + b \rightarrow b = 6$.

   The $y -$intercept of the line is 4. The equation of the line is: $y = -x + 6$.

3) What is the equation of the line that passes through $(6, -3)$ and has a slope of 5?

   Solution: The general slope-intercept form of the equation of a line is:

   $y = mx + b$, where m is the slope and b is the $y -$intercept.

   By substituting the given point and slope, we obtain:

   $y = mx + b \rightarrow -3 = (5)(6) + b$. So, $b = -3 - 30 = -33$,

   the required equation of the line is: $y = 5x - 33$.

Graph an Equation in the Standard Form

A two-dimensional graph comprises two intersecting lines, known as the x-axis (horizontal) and the y-axis (vertical). The intersection of these two axes is known as the origin. A point's location on the graph is given by a pair of coordinates, (x, y).

By connecting two points on this graph, a line can be formed.

The standard form of a linear equation is represented as Ax + By = C.

In this equation, the variables A, B, and C are replaced with real numbers. The variable x typically represents the independent variable, while y represents the dependent variable.

When an equation is in standard form, it may not provide the slope and y-intercept directly, making it challenging to graph the equation immediately. In such cases, specific methods are used to determine these values.

There are 2 different methods to graph a line in standard form:

- **First method:** involves converting the equation to slope-intercept form ($y = mx + b$) and then graph it.

- **Second method:** entails finding the x and y −intercepts of the line in standard form, connecting these two intercepts, and drawing the line accordingly (easiest way).

Keep in mind that at the y −intercept, the coordinate of x is equal to zero and that at the x-intercept, the coordinate of y is equal to zero. When you want to find the y −intercept, put x equal to zero and solve for y. When you want to find the x −intercept, set y equal to zero and solve for x. Then find the 2 intercepts on the coordinate plane and draw the line on the graph.

Example:

✎ Graph the following equation: $3x - 2y = 12$

Solution: First, find the x −intercept:

$y = 0 \rightarrow 3x - 2(0) = 12 \rightarrow 3x = 12 \rightarrow$

$x = 4$. coordinates are (4,0).

Now, find the y −intercept:

$x = 0 \rightarrow 3(0) - 2y = 12 \rightarrow -2y = 12 \rightarrow$

$y = -6$. coordinates are $(0, -6)$.

Now, find (4,0) and $(0, -6)$ on the

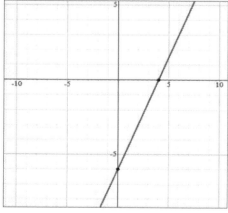

coordinate plane, and draw the line between these two points on the graph.

Graphing Linear Inequalities

Graphing linear inequalities is like graphing linear equations, but with the added aspect of shading to represent a range of values that satisfy the inequality. Here's a step-by-step guide to graphing linear inequalities:

- ✓ To graph a linear inequality, begin by plotting the graph of the corresponding "equals" line.
- ✓ Use a dash line for less than ($<$) and greater than ($>$) signs and a solid line for less than and equal to ($\leq$) and greater than and equal to ($\geq$).
- ✓ Choose a testing point. This point can be of any value on either side of the line. Substitute the coordinates of the testing point (x, y) into the original inequality. If the inequality holds true, the region of the line containing the testing point is part of the solution. However, if the values do not satisfy the inequality, the other region of the line is the solution.

Example:

✎ Sketch the graph of inequality: $y < 3x - 2$.

Solution: To draw the graph of $y < 3x - 2$, you first need to graph the line:

$y = 3x - 2$.

Since there is a less than ($<$) sign, draw a dash line.

The slope is 3 and $y-$intercept is 2.

Then, choose a testing point and substitute the value of x and y from that point into the inequality. The easiest point to test is the origin: (0,0).

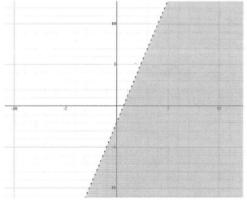

$(0,0) \rightarrow y < 3x - 2 \rightarrow 0 < 3(0) - 2 \rightarrow 0 < -2$.

This is not correct! Since the origin makes the inequality false, you would shade the region that does not include the origin, which is the region above the line $y = 3x - 2$. So, the graph of the inequality $y < 3x - 2$ consists of a dashed line $y = 3x - 2$, with shading above the line

Write an Equation from a Graph

To express an equation of a line in slope-intercept form, follow these steps using a graph of the equation:

1. Select any two points on the line.
2. Determine the slope of the line using the selected points. This slope value represents the variable "m" in the equation.
3. Identify the coordinates of the y-intercept. It should be in the form $(0, b)$, where the y-coordinate represents the value of "b" in the equation.
4. Formulate the equation by substituting the determined numerical values for "m" and b.
5. To validate the equation, choose a point on the line (excluding the y-intercept) and substitute its coordinates into the equation. Check if the equation holds true for that point.

Example:

✎ Write the equation of the following line in slope-intercept form:

Solution: Suppose we have the points $(3, 4)$ and $(6, -2)$ on the line. First, the slope (m) using the given points:

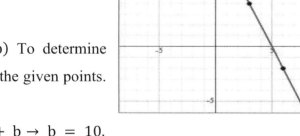

$m = \frac{4-(-2)}{3-6} = \frac{6}{-3} = -2.$

Next, find the $y-$intercept $(0, b)$ To determine the value of b, we can use one of the given points. Let's use the first point $(3, 4)$:

$4 = -2(3) + b \rightarrow 4 = -6 + b \rightarrow b = 10.$

Therefore, the equation of this line is:

$$y = -2x + 10.$$

Now, let's check the equation by picking another point on the line. Let's choose point (1,8). Then:

$(1,8) \rightarrow y = -2x + 10 \rightarrow 8 = -2(1) + 10 \rightarrow 8 = 8.$ This is true.

Slope-intercept Form and Point-slope Form

The slope-intercept form is a way to express linear equations. It has the general form:

$$y = mx + b$$

- y and x are the variables.

- m is the slope of the line.

- b is the y-intercept, that is the point where the line crosses the y-axis.

The point-slope form of the equation is given by: $y - y^1 = m(x - x^1)$.

This form is useful when we have information about one point on the line (x_1, y_1), and the slope of the line: m. The slope intercept form is probably the most frequently used way to express the equation of a line.

Examples:

1) Find the equation of a line with point (2,3) and slope -3, and write it in slope-intercept and point-slope forms.

   Solution: Using point-slope form, we have the point and slope:

   $x^1 = 2, y^1 = 3$, and m $= -2$.

   Then:$y - y_1 = m(x - x_1) \rightarrow y - 3 = -2(x - 2)$

   The slope-intercept form of a line is:$y = mx + b$

   Since y = 3, x = 2, m = -2, we just need to solve for b

   $$y = mx + b \rightarrow 3 = -2(2) + b \rightarrow b = 7$$

   Slope-intercept form:$y = -2x + 7$

2) Find the equation of a line with point (3,4) and slope 5, and write it in slope-intercept and point-slope forms.

   Solution: Using point-slope form, we have the point and slope:

   $x^1 = 3, y^1 = 4$, and $m = 5$.

   Then:$y - y_1 = m(x - x_1) \rightarrow y - 4 = 5(x - 3)$

   The slope-intercept form of a line is: $y = mx + b$

   Since y = 4, x = 3, m = 5, we just need to solve for b

   $y = mx + b \rightarrow 4 = 5(3) + b \rightarrow b = -11$

   Slope-intercept form:$y = 4x - 11$

Write a Point-slope Form Equation from a Graph

The point-slope form equation is used to determine the equation of a straight line when given a specific point. It is applicable when both the slope of the line and a point on the line are known. To find the equation of a line with a slope $'m'$ that passes through the point (x^1, y^1), the point-slope formula can be used.

The point-slope form equation is expressed as $y - y_1 = m(x - x_1)$ where (x, y) is any random point on the line, and 'm' represents the slope of the line.

To find and solve the point-slope form equation of a straight line, follow these steps:

- 1st step: Find the slope, 'm' of the straight line and the coordinates (x_1, y_1) of the random point on the line. The slope formula is $m = \frac{change\ in\ y}{change\ in\ x}$.

- 2nd step: Put the values you found in the first step in the point-slope formula:
$$y - y_1 = m(x - x_1)$$

- 3rd step: Simplify the equation to get the line's equation in the standard form.

Example:

✎ According to the following graph, what is the equation of the line in point-slope form?

Solution: First, you should find the slope of the line (m). The coordinate of the red point is $(2,3)$. Consider another random point on the line such as $(5,4)$. Put this value in the slope formula: $m = \frac{change\ in\ y}{change\ in\ x} = \frac{4-3}{5-2} = \frac{1}{3} \rightarrow m = \frac{1}{3}$.

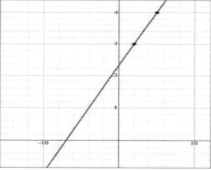

Now write the equation in point-slope form using the coordinate of the red point is $(2,3)$ and $m = \frac{1}{3}$:

$$y - y_1 = m(x - x_1) \rightarrow y - 3 = \frac{1}{3}(x - 2).$$

Therefore, the equation of the line in point-slope form is $y - 3 = \frac{1}{3}(x - 2)$.

Intercepts (x and y −intercept)

The linear equations' standard form (the general form) is described as $Ax + By = C$.

In this form of the equation, A, B, and C are integers, and the letters x and y are considered the variables.

When you need to have a linear equation in the standard form, you can easily change it in a way that can be represented in the form $Ax + By = C$. Keep in mind that A, B, and C should be integers and the order of the variables should be as mentioned in the standard form's equation.

- x −**intercept:** the x −value when the line intersects the x −axis. In this case, y is equal to zero.

- y −**intercept**: the y −value where the line intersects the y −axis. In this case, x is equal to zero.

Examples:

1) Find the x − and y −intercepts of line $6x + 24y = 12$.

   Solution: To find the x −intercept, you can consider y equal to 0 and solve for x:

   $6x + 24y = 12 \rightarrow 6x + 24(0) = 12 \rightarrow 6x = 12 \rightarrow x = 2$ (x −intercept)

   To find the y −intercept, you can consider x equal to 0 and solve for y:

   $6x + 24y = 12 \rightarrow 6(0) + 24y = 12 \rightarrow 24y = 12 \rightarrow y = \frac{1}{2}$ (y −intercept)

   Then, the x −intercept is 2, and the y −intercept is $\frac{1}{2}$.

2) Find the x- and y-intercepts of the line $2x - 3y = 9$

   Solution: To find the x −intercept, you can consider y equal to 0 and solve for x:

   $2x - 3y = 9 \rightarrow 2x - 3(0) = 9 \rightarrow 2x = 9 \rightarrow x = \frac{9}{2}$ (x −intercept)

   To find the y −intercept, you can consider x equal to 0 and solve for y:

   $2x - 3y = 9 \rightarrow 2(0) - 3y = 9 \rightarrow -3y = 9 \rightarrow y = -3$.

   The y −intercept is -3

   Therefore, for the line $2x - 3y = 9$, the x −intercept is $\frac{9}{2}$ and the y −intercept is -3.

Equations of Horizontal and Vertical lines

Horizontal lines have a slope of 0 in the slope-intercept form equation, $y = mx + b$. When the slope (m) is 0, the equation simplifies to $y = b$, where b represents the y-coordinate of the $y - intercept$.

Similarly, in the graph of a vertical line, the $x - coordinate$ only takes one specific value. Therefore, the equation for a vertical line can be expressed as $x = a$, where a represents the specific value that x takes.

Examples:

1) Write an equation for the horizontal line that passes through (7,3).

   Solution: Since the line is horizontal, the equation of the line is in the form of:

   y = b.

   Where y always takes the same value of 3.

   Thus, the equation of the line is:

   y = 3.

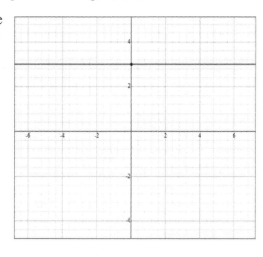

2) Write an equation for the vertical line that passes through $(-3,7)$.

   Solution: Since the line is vertical, the equation of the line is in the form of:

   x = a. Where x always takes the same value of -3.

   Thus, the equation of the line is: $x = -3$

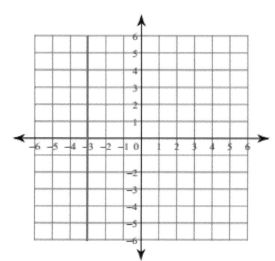

Graph a Horizontal or Vertical line.

When you graph a line, you usually need a point and the slope of the line to draw the line on the coordinate plane. But there are also exceptions that are called horizontal and vertical lines.

A horizontal line is a straight line that extends from left to right. An example of a horizontal line is the x-axis. The slope of a horizontal line is always zero because the slope is defined as "rise over run," and for a horizontal line, the rise is 0. When dividing 0 by any number, the result is always 0. Thus, the slope of a horizontal line is consistently zero. Horizontal lines are always parallel to the x-axis and can be written in the form $y = a$, where "a" represents a real number.

The vertical line is a straight line that extends up and down. An example of a vertical line is the $y - axis$. The slope of a vertical line is always undefined because the run of a vertical line is 0. Dividing any number by 0 is undefined. Consequently, the slope of a vertical line is always undefined. Vertical lines are always parallel to the y-axis and can be written in the form $x = a$, where "a" represents a real number.

Examples:

1) Graph this equation: $y = -3$

   Solution: $y = -3$ is a horizontal line and this equation tells you that every $y -$value is -3. You can consider some points that have a $y -$value of -3, then draw a line that connects the points.

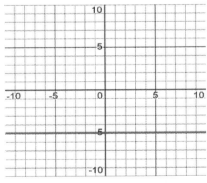

2) Graph this equation: $x = 2$

   Solution: $x = 2$ is a vertical line and this equation tells you that every $x -$value is 2. You can consider some points that have an $x -$value of 2, then draw a line that connects the points.

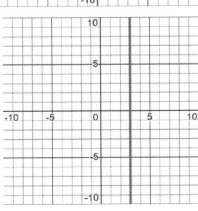

Graph an Equation in Point-Slope Form

The point-slope form represents the equation of a straight line using a slope and a point on that line. It allows us to find the equation of a line with slope m that passes through the point (x_1, y_1) .

The equation in point-slope form is $y - y_1 = m(x - x_1)$. represents a point on the line and m is the slope of the line.

To graph an equation in point-slope form, follow these steps:

- 1st step: Ensure that the equation in point-slope form uses subtraction as specified in the point-slope form formula. If one side of the equation does not use subtraction, rewrite it accordingly.

- 2nd step: Find a random point on the straight line and the slope of the line. The slope formula is $m = \dfrac{\text{change in } y}{\text{change in } x}$.

- 3rd step: Use the random point and the value of the slope to graph the line.

Example:

✎ Graph the following line: $y - 3 = -\frac{1}{3}(x + 4)$

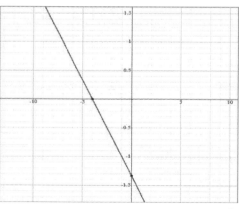

Solution: First, check the point-slope form equation. If one side of the equation doesn't use subtraction operation, you should rewrite it with the subtraction sign: $y - 3 = -\frac{1}{3}(x + 4) \rightarrow y - 3 = -\frac{1}{3}(x + 4)$. Find a random point on the straight line and the slope of the line. You can use the point that is used in the formula: $(x_1, y_1) \rightarrow (-4, 3)$. The slope is $-\frac{1}{3}$. Use the random point and the value of slope to graph the line: find the point $(-4, 3)$ on the coordinate plane. The slope is $-\frac{1}{3}$ and is the same as $\frac{-1}{3}$. So, move down 1 unit and right 3 units to find the other point on the straight line: $(-2, 2)$. Connect these two points and graph the line.

Equation of Parallel and Perpendicular Lines

To understand the equations of parallel and perpendicular lines, it's essential to know the concept of slope.

- ✓ Parallel lines have the same slope. This means that if two lines are parallel, their slopes are equal.

- ✓ Perpendicular lines have slopes that are opposite reciprocals of each other. If the slope of one line is represented as m, the slope of the perpendicular line is $-\frac{1}{m}$. In other words, two lines are perpendicular only if the product of their slopes is equal to -1. $m^1 \times m^2 = -1$.

- ✓ A vertical line has an undefined slope. A horizontal line perpendicular to it has a slope of 0.

Examples:

Find the equation of a line that is:

1) Parallel to $y = 5x - 3$ and passes though the point $(4, -1)$.

   Solution: The slope of $y = 5x - 3$ is 5. We can solve it using the "point-slope" equation of a line: $y - y_1 = 5(x - x_1)$ and then put in the point $(4, -1)$:

   $y - (-1) = 5(x - 4)$.

   You can also write it in slope intercept format: $y = mx + b$.

   $y + 1 = 5x - 20 \rightarrow y = 5x - 21$.

2) Perpendicular to $y = -3x + 8$ and passes though the point $(6, -1)$.

   Solution: The given line has a slope of -3. The perpendicular line will have a slope that is the negative reciprocal of -3, which is $\frac{1}{3}$. Using the point-slope equation and the given point $(6, -1)$, Then: $y - y_1 = \left(\frac{1}{3}\right)(x - x_1)$ and now put in the point $(6, -1)$: $y + 1 = \left(\frac{1}{3}\right)(x - 6)$.

   Slope intercept $y = mx + b$ form:

$$y + 1 = \frac{x}{3} - \frac{6}{3} \rightarrow y = \frac{1}{3}x - 3$$

Compare Linear Function's Graph and Equations

- ✓ A linear function can be expressed in the form $f(x) = mx + b$. where m and b are real numbers.

- ✓ A linear graph visually represents a linear function by connecting points plotted on the coordinate plane with a straight line.

- ✓ To compare a linear function's graph and a linear equation, you can examine the slope or the y-intercept of both.

- ✓ To compare slopes between a linear function's graph and a linear equation, determine the change in y and the change in x between any two points on the line. Then use the slope formula $\left(m = \frac{change\ in\ y}{change\ in\ x}\right)$ to calculate the value of m. Once you find the value of m, you can compare it with the slope value in the linear equation.

- ✓ To compare the y-intercept between the linear function's graph and a linear equation, first, determine the value of b on the graph. This is done by identifying the point at which the line intersects the y-axis. Then, compare the b-value of the graph with the y-intercept (b-value) of the linear equation.

Example:

Function A

Function B

$y = 2x - 8$

✎ Compare the slope of function A and function B.

Solution: First, find the slope(m) of function A. Find the change in y and the change in x points $(2,0)$ and $(0, -6)$ on the line:

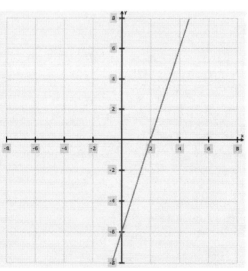

$m = \frac{change\ in\ y}{change\ in\ x} : \frac{-6-0}{0-2} = 3.$

Now, find the slope of function B. The equation of function B in the slope-intercept form is $y = 2x - 8$. Therefore, its slope is equal to 2. In the final step, compare the slopes. The slope of function A is 3 and is greater than the slope of function $B(2)$.

Graphing Absolute Value Equations

Graphing absolute value equations involves understanding the basic shape of the absolute value function (Its graph is a "V" shape) and then applying transformations based on the given equation. The graphing form of a linear absolute value function is given by:

$$y = |mx + b| + c$$

✓ The vertex, which represents the lowest or highest point on the graph, is located at the coordinates $\left(\frac{-b}{m}, c\right)$.

✓ A vertical line that divides the graph into two equal halves can be found at:
$x = -\frac{b}{m}$.

✓ To graph an absolute value equation, find the vertex and some other points by substituting some values for x and solving for y.

✓ Remember that the shape will always be a V, but its position, direction, and steepness can vary based on the equation.

Example:

✎ Graph $y = |x + 3|$.

Solution: Find the vertex $\left(\frac{-b}{m}, c\right)$.

According to the general form of an absolute value function:

$y = |mx + b| + c$.

We have:

$x = \frac{-b}{m} \rightarrow x = \frac{-3}{1} = -3.$

And c is zero then the point $(-3, 0)$ is the vertex of the graph.

and represents the center of the table of values. Create the table and plot the ordered pairs.

Now, find the points and graph the equation.

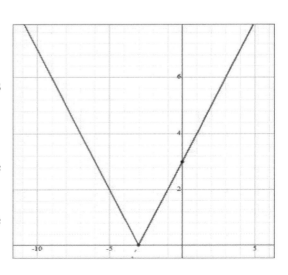

Two-variable Linear Equations' Word Problems

A two-variable linear equation is an equation that involves two variables, typically represented by x and y, with an exponent of 1. The solutions to a two-variable linear equation can be expressed as ordered pairs (x, y).

A two-variables linear equation can be seen in various forms like standard form, point-slope form, and intercept form:

- Standard form: $ax + by = c$. In this form, a, b, and c are real numbers, while x and y are the variables.

- The slope-intercept form of a two-variables linear equation is as $y = mx + b$. In this form of the equation, m is the line's slope and b is the y−intercept of the line.

- The point-slope form of a two-variables linear equation is as $y - y_1 = m(x - x_1)$. In this form of the equation, (x, y) is a given point on the line and m is the line's slope.

To write and solve a two-variables linear equation word problem you can follow these steps:

- 1st step: Read the question carefully, identifying the given information and what is being asked in the problem.

- 2nd step: Determine the unknowns in the question and show them by x, and y variables.

- 3rd step: Change the words of the problem to the mathematical language or math expression.

- 4th step: Create a two-variable linear equation using the given information from the problem.

- 5th step: In the last step, solve the equation to find the value of the unknowns.

Example:

✎ Elvin is going to buy a box of candies as a gift for his friend. He can add as many candies as he wants to this box at a price of $5 per number. He also plans to buy a beautiful painting for $50 as a gift. Show in an equation how the total cost, y, depends on the number of candies, x.

Solution: The cost of each candy $= \$5$ and the cost of the painting $= \$250$. Here, the number of candies is unknown, and we consider the variable x for it, and we show the total cost with the variable y. Therefore, our two-variable linear equation will be as follows: $y = 5x + 50$.

Chapter 6: Quadratic Equations

 Mathematical concepts covered:

- Solving a Quadratic Equations
- Graphing Quadratic Functions
- Solve a Quadratic Equation by Factoring
- Transformations of Quadratic Functions
- Quadratic Formula and the Discriminant
- Characteristics of Quadratic Functions
- Characteristics of Quadratic Functions
- Complete a Function Table
- Domain and Range of Quadratic Functions
- Factor Quadratics: Special Cases
- Factor Quadratics Using Algebra Tiles
- Quadratic Function Vertex and Point

Solving a Quadratic Equations

Quadratic equations are polynomial equations of degree 2. They are typically in the form:

$$ax^2 + bx + c = 0 \text{ (Where a, b, and c are constants, and a is not equal to zero)}$$

There are various methods to solve quadratic equations:

❖ Factorize, if possible, by finding two binomial factors that multiply to give the quadratic equation. Set each factor equal to zero and solve for x.

❖ If the quadratic cannot be factorized, use the quadratic formula to find the solutions for x. Quadratic formula: $x = \frac{-b \pm \sqrt{b^2 - 4ac}}{2a}$.

❖ Completing the Square: This method involves rewriting the quadratic equation in the form $((x - h)^2 = k)$, from which you can easily solve for x.

Examples:

✎ Find the solutions of each quadratic.

1) $3x^2 + 5x + 2 = 0$.

We need to find two numbers for factoring whose sum is 5 (from $5x$) and whose product is 6 (from a times c). Those numbers are 3 and 2. So, we can rewrite the equation as $3x^2 + 3x + 2x + 2 = 0$.

Now, let's group the terms and factor: $3x^2 + 3x + 2x + 2 = 0$

$(3x^2 + 3x) + (2x + 2) = 0 \rightarrow 3x(x + 1) + 2(x + 1) = 0$

$\rightarrow (x + 1)(3x + 2) = 0$. Now, the product of two expressions is 0

$x + 1 = 0 \rightarrow x = -1; \qquad 3x + 2 = 0 \rightarrow x = -\frac{2}{3}$

2) $2x^2 - 5x - 3 = 0$.

Use quadratic formula: $x_{1,2} = \frac{-b \pm \sqrt{b^2 - 4ac}}{2a}$, $a = 12, b = -5$ and $c = -3$.

Then: $x_{1,2} = \frac{-(-5) \pm \sqrt{(-5)^2 - 4 \times 2(-3)}}{2(2)} \rightarrow \begin{cases} x_1 = \frac{5 + \sqrt{25 + 24}}{4} = \frac{5 + \sqrt{49}}{4} = \frac{5 + 7}{4} = 3 \\ x_2 = \frac{5 - \sqrt{25 + 24}}{4} = \frac{5 - \sqrt{49}}{4} = \frac{5 - 7}{4} = -\frac{1}{2} \end{cases}$

3) $x^2 - 4x - 5 = 0$

Rewriting as: $(x^2 - 4x = 5)$; Add 4 to both sides (half of 4 squared) to complete the square: $(x^2 - 4x + 4 = 9) \rightarrow (x - 2)^2 = 9$

Taking square root of both sides: $(x - 2 = \pm 3)$. So, $(x = 5)$ or $(x = -1)$

Graphing Quadratic Functions

Quadratic functions in vertex form: $y = a(x - h)^2 + k$ where (h, k) is the vertex of the function. The axis of symmetry is $x = h$.

Quadratic functions in standard form: $y = ax^2 + bx + c$ where $x = -\frac{b}{2a}$ is the value of x in the vertex of the function.

To graph a quadratic function, start by finding the vertex, which can be obtained from the standard form by using the formula $x = -\frac{b}{2a}$ and substituting this value into the equation to find the corresponding y value. The vertex represents the lowest or highest point on the graph, depending on the coefficient aa. The graph of a quadratic function is a U-shaped curve called a "parabola".

After finding the vertex, you can choose some values for x (usually around the vertex) and solve for y to obtain other points on the graph.

Example:

✎ Sketch the graph of $y = (x + 3)^2 - 5$.

Quadratic functions in vertex form:

$y = a(x - h)^2 + k$, and (h, k) is the vertex.

Then, the vertex of $y = (x + 3)^2 - 5$ is: $(-3, -5)$.

Substitute zero for x and solve for y:

$y = (0 + 3)^2 - 5 = 4$.

The $y -$ intercept is $(0, 4)$.

Now, you can simply graph the quadratic function.

Notice that quadratic function is a $U -$shaped curve.

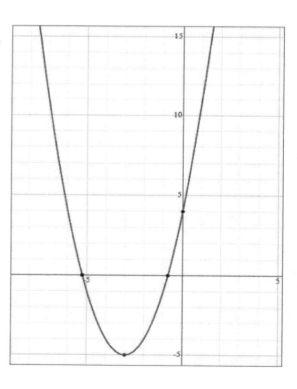

Solve a Quadratic Equation by Factoring

The general form of a quadratic equation is: $ax^2 + bx + c = 0$.

When factoring a quadratic equation, the multiplication property of zero (MPZ) can be used.

The MPZ states that if $p \times q = 0$, then either $p = 0$ or $q = 0$.

When there are only two terms in a quadratic equation and they have a common factor, factoring becomes relatively simple. This is true for quadratic equations in the form $ax^2 + bx + c = 0$, where the value of c is 0. The two terms have at least a common factor of x. In this case, the steps to solve the equation are as follows:

 a. Find the greatest common factor (GCF) and factor it out.

 b. Use the multiplication property of zero (MPZ) to solve the equation.

☑ Remember, not all quadratic equations can be easily factored, especially if they have non-integer or complex solutions. In such cases, other methods such as completing the square, using the quadratic formula, or graphing might be more appropriate.

Examples:

1) Find the solutions of $x^2 - 9x = 0$.

Solution: The greatest common factor of the two terms is x.

Take the common factor out:

$$x(x - 9) = 0.$$

Using MPZ, which states that either $x = 0$ or $x - 9 = 0$.

In the second equation, the value of x equals 9.

$$x - 9 = 0 \rightarrow x = 9.$$

2) Solve $x^2 + 2x - 15 = 0$ by factoring.

Solution: We first factorize the expression:

$$x^2 + 2x - 15 = (x + 5)(x - 3) = 0.$$

using MPZ, which states that either $(x + 5) = 0$ or $(x - 3) = 0$.

$$(x + 5) = 0 \rightarrow x = -5, (x - 3) = 0 \rightarrow x = 3.$$

Transformations of Quadratic Functions

In the quadratic equation $y = ax^2$, the graph stretches vertically by the value of unit a.

Note that if a is negative, the graph will be inverted.

In the standard form, the quadratic function is as follows:

$f(x) = a(x - h)^2 + k$. In this form, the vertex of the graph is located at the point (h, k)

❖ If $k > 0$, the graph moves upwards, and if $k < 0$, the graph moves down.

❖ If $h > 0$, the graph moves to the right, and if $h < 0$, the graph moves to the left.

The value of a indicates the elongation of the graph.

❖ If $|a| > 1$, the points corresponding to a specific value of xx move farther from the x-axis, resulting in a thinner

❖ If $|a| < 1$, the points corresponding to a specific value of xx get closer to the x-axis, resulting in a wider graph.

Example:

✍ State the transformations and sketch the graph of the following function.

$y = -2(x + 1)^2 + 4$

In this example, since $x - h = x + 1$, then $h = -1$. In this equation, $a = -2$, $h = -1$ and $k = 4$. Since $a < 0$, there is a downward parabola. The vertex is at $(-1, 4)$.

Find the vertex and some other points to graph the parabola.

$x = 0 \rightarrow y = -2(0 + 1)^2 + 4 = 2$,

$x = -1 \rightarrow y = -2(-1 + 1)^2 + 4 = 4$,

$x = -3 \rightarrow y = -2(-3 + 1)^2 + 4 = 8$.

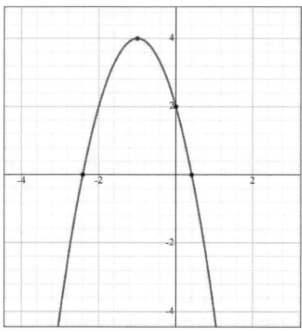

Quadratic Formula and the Discriminant

A quadratic equation is in the form of is typically written in the form:

$ax^2 + bx + c = 0$.

To solve a quadratic equation by the delta (discriminant) method, go through the following steps:

Step 1: Calculate the delta number as follows: $\Delta = b^2 - 4ac$.

Step 2: Depending on the value of delta, there are three possible outcomes:

- If $\Delta < 0$, then the quadratic equation has no real roots. It means that the graph of the quadratic equation does not intersect the x-axis.

- If $\Delta > 0$, then the quadratic equation has two roots, which are obtained by the following formulas:

  $x_1 = \frac{-b - \sqrt{\Delta}}{2a}$ and $x_2 = \frac{-b + \sqrt{\Delta}}{2a}$. These formulas give the values of x at which the quadratic equation crosses the x −axis.

- If $\Delta = 0$, then the two roots of the equation are equal and are called double roots:

  $x_1 = x_2 = \frac{-b}{2a}$. The graph of the quadratic equation touches the x −axis at a single point.

Examples:

1) Solve equation $2x^2 + 5x - 3 = 0$.

   Solution: To solve a quadratic equation, first find the values of a, b, c.

   By comparing the mentioned equation with the equation $ax^2 + bx + c = 0$, the values a, b, c are equal to: $a = 2, b = 5, c = -3$.

   Now, calculate delta (Δ). Given the values of a, b, c, the value of Δ is equal to:

   $\Delta = b^2 - 4ac = 5^2 - 4 \times 2 \times (-3) = 25 + 24 = 49$.

   49 is a positive number. Therefore, this equation will have two different solutions:

   $x = \frac{-5 \pm \sqrt{49}}{4} \rightarrow x = \frac{-5 \pm 7}{4} \rightarrow x = -\frac{-5 - 7}{4} = -3$, or $x = \frac{-5 + 7}{4} = \frac{1}{2}$.

Characteristics of Quadratic Functions

Quadratic functions are of the form ($f(x) = ax^2 + bx + c$), where (a), (b), and (c) are constants, and (a) is not equal to zero. Here are the primary characteristics of quadratic functions:

1) **Parabolic Shape:** the graph of a quadratic function is a parabola. If ($a > 0$), the parabola opens upwards, and if ($a < 0$), it opens downwards.

2) **Vertex:** the vertex is the highest or lowest point of the parabola, depending on its orientation. The x-coordinate of the vertex can be found using the formula ($h = -\frac{b}{2a}$) The y-coordinate is then ($f(h)$).

   - The form ($f(x) = a(x - h)^2 + k$) represents a quadratic function where ((h, k)) is the vertex.

3) **Axis of Symmetry:** the parabola is symmetrical about a vertical line called the axis of symmetry. The equation for the axis of symmetry is ($x = -\frac{b}{2a}$), which is also the x-coordinate of the vertex.

4) **Y-intercept:** The point where the graph crosses the y-axis. It can be found by setting ($x = 0$) in the equation, resulting in the point ($(0, c)$).

5) **X-intercepts** (Roots or Zeroes): points where the graph intersects the x-axis. Depending on the discriminant ($b^2 - 4ac$):

   - If the discriminant is greater than 0, there are two distinct real roots.

   - If the discriminant is equal to 0, there is one real root (the vertex lies on the x-axis).

   - If the discriminant is less than 0, there are no real roots (the graph doesn't cross the x-axis).

6) **Direction:** as mentioned, if ($a > 0$), the parabola opens upwards, indicating the function has a minimum value. Conversely, if ($a < 0$), the parabola opens downwards, indicating a maximum value. The y-value of the vertex is the minimum or maximum value of the function.

7) **Range:** as (x) approaches positive or negative infinity:

- If ($a > 0$), ($f(x)$) approaches positive infinity.

- If ($a < 0$), ($f(x)$) approaches negative infinity.

8) **Width and Compression:** the value of ($|a|$) affects the "width" of the parabola. If ($|a| > 1$), the graph is narrower than ($y = x^2$). If ($0 < |a| < 1$), the graph is wider than ($y = x^2$).

Understanding these characteristics can help you sketch the graph of a quadratic function and interpret real-world applications involving quadratics.

Example:

✎ Specify characteristics of the vertex, direction, and y −intercept for the quadratic function $f(x) = 4x^2 - 6x + 2$.

Solution: In the standard form of a quadratic function $f(x) = ax^2 + bx + c$, the vertex is not immediately obvious. The x −coordinate for the vertex can be obtained by using the formula: $x = -\frac{b}{2a}$,

$$x = -\frac{-6}{2(4)} = \frac{3}{4}$$

Now, substitute it into the equation of function to obtain the y −coordinate:

$$y = f\left(\frac{3}{4}\right) = 2\left(\frac{3}{4}\right)^2 - 3\left(\frac{3}{4}\right) + 1$$

$$= 2\left(\frac{9}{16}\right) - \frac{9}{4} + 1$$

$$= \frac{9}{8} - \frac{9}{4} + 1 = -\frac{1}{8}.$$

So, the vertex of the function $f(x) = 2x^2 - 3x + 1$ is the ordered pair $\left(\frac{3}{4}, -\frac{1}{8}\right)$.

Remember that the sign of the coefficient x^2 indicates the direction of the quadratic equation. Since the coefficient of x^2 is 2, then it is upward.

To find the y −intercept of a function, evaluate the output at $f(0)$.

$$f(0) = 2(0)^2 - 3(0) + 1 = 1.$$

Characteristics of Quadratic Functions:

From the graph of a quadratic function, determine the:

- vertex
- axis of symmetry
- x −intercepts
- y −intercept
- domain
- range
- minimum/maximum value

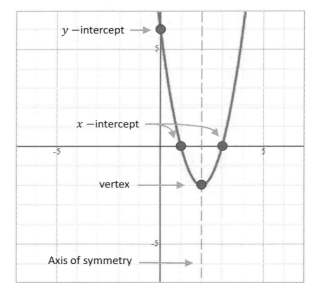

Example:

🖎 Considering the following graph, determine the following:

- vertex
- axis of symmetry
- x −intercepts
- y −intercept
- Max/minimum point.

Solution: According to the graph, see that a point at the coordinate $(-2,2)$ is the vertex. So, the line $x = -2$ is the axis of symmetry.

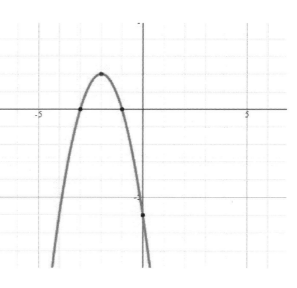

Since the graph intersects the x −axis at points -1 and -3, the mentioned points are x −intercepts. In the same way, the point $(0, -6)$ is the y −intercept.

In addition, this is clear that the vertex is the maximum point.

Complete a Function Table

Completing a function table is a systematic way to evaluate a function for various inputs (often denoted as x values) to obtain the corresponding outputs (often denoted as $f(x)$ or y values). To complete a function table of the quadratic function:

Step 1: Consider the input and output in the table.

Step 2: Substitute the input into the function.

Step 3: Evaluate the output by performing the necessary calculations based on the substituted input value.

This method helps visualize how a function behaves across different input values and is particularly helpful when preparing to graph a function.

Example:

✎ Complete the table.

$g(t) = t^2 - 2t + 1$	
t	$g(t)$
-2	
0	
2	

Solution: According to the function table, the first value of the input in the table is -1. Evaluate $g(t) = t^2 - 2t + 1$ for t $= -2$

g$(-2) = (-2)^2 - 2(-2) + 1$

$= 4 + 4 + 1 = 9$.

When t $= -2$, then g$(-2) = 9$. Complete the first row of the table.

In the same way, evaluate $g(t) = t^2 - 2t + 1$ for t $= 0$ and t $= 1$, respectively. So,

g$(0) = (0)^2 - 2(0) + 1 = 1$,

g$(2) = (2)^2 - 2(2) + 1 = 1$.

Enter the obtained values in the table.

$g(t) = t^2 - 2t + 1$	
t	$g(t)$
-2	9
0	1
2	1

Domain and Range of Quadratic Functions

The domain of any quadratic function in the form $y = ax^2 + bx + c$ (where a, b, and c are constants) is the set of all real numbers.

To determine the range of a quadratic function, follow these steps:

- Identify the vertex of the parabola: The vertex is the point on the graph where the quadratic function reaches its maximum or minimum value. It can be found using the formula for the vertex: Vertex $(h, k) = (-\frac{b}{2a}, f(-\frac{b}{2a}))$.

- Determine the direction of the parabola: Examine the coefficient aa in the quadratic function. If $a > 0$, the parabola opens upwards, and the vertex represents the minimum point of the function. If $a < 0$, the parabola opens downwards, and the vertex represents the maximum point of the function.

Example:

✍ What is the domain and range of the function to the equation?
$$y = 2x^2 - 4x + 2.$$

We'll first identify the vertex and determine the direction of the parabola.
The vertex of a quadratic function can be found using the formula:

Vertex $(h, k) = \left(-\frac{b}{2a}, f\left(-\frac{b}{2a}\right)\right)$.

In our case, the quadratic function is $y = 2x^2 - 4x + 2$ where a $= 2$, b $= -4$, and c $= 1$.

h $= \frac{-(-4)}{2 \times 2} = \frac{2}{2} = 1$; k = f(h) = f(1) = $2(1)^2 - 4(1) + 2 = 2 - 4 + 2 = 0$

So, the vertex of the parabola is $(1, 0)$.

Since the coefficient a is positive (a $= 1 > 0$), the parabola opens upwards, and the vertex is the minimum point of the function.

The domain of a quadratic function is all real numbers since it is defined for every x value. Therefore, the domain is: Domain $= \{x \mid x \in R\}$

The range is determined by the direction of the parabola and the vertex. Since the parabola opens upwards, the range will include all values greater than or equal to the $y-$ coordinate (k) of the vertex. In this case, the range will be:
Range $= \{y \mid y \geq 0\}$

Factor Quadratics: Special Cases

Special cases square:

- Factor an equation of the form: $a^2 \pm 2ab + b^2 = (a \pm b)^2$

- Factor an equation of the form: $a^2 - b^2 = (a + b)(a - b)$

Examples:

1) Factor $3x^2 - 49$.

   Notice that $3x^2$ and 49 are perfect squares, because $3x^2 = \left(\sqrt{3}x\right)^2$, and $49 = 7^2$. By using the formula $a^2 - b^2 = (a + b)(a - b)$. Let $a = \sqrt{3}.x$, and $b = 3$. The represented equation can be rewritten as follow:

   $3x^2 - 49 = \left(\sqrt{3}x + 7\right)\left(\sqrt{3}x - 7\right)$.

2) Factor $k^2 - 2k + 1$.

   First, observe that k^2 and 1 are perfect squares, as $k^2 = k^2$ and $1 = 1^2$. This implies that $a = k$ and $b = 1$. Next, check if the middle term is equal to $2ab$, which it is: $2ab = 2(k)(1) = 2k$. Therefore, the equation can be rewritten as:

   $k^2 - 2k + 1 = (k - 1)^2$.

3) Factor $9x^2 + 12x + 4$.

   First, notice that $9x^2$ and 4 are perfect squares because $9x^2 = (3x)^2$ and $4 = 2^2$. Let $a = 3x$, and $b = 2$. Now, evaluate the middle term $12x$. Then, you can write as $12x = 2(3x)2 = 2ab$. Using this formula: $a^2 + 2ab + b^2 = (a + b)^2$. Therefore, we have:

   $9x^2 + 12x + 4 = (3x + 2)^2$.

4) Factor $4x^2 - 16x + 16$.

   First, rewrite the equation as $4x^2 - 16x + 16 = 4(x^2 - 4x + 4)$. According to the x^2 and 4 are perfect squares because $x^2 = (x)^2$ and $4 = 2^2$. That is, $a = x$, and $b = 2$. Now, check to see if the middle term is equal to $2ab$: $2(x)2 = 4x$. Using this formula: $a^2 + 2ab + b^2 = (a + b)^2$. Therefore, we have:

   $4x^2 - 16x + 16 = 4(x^2 - 4x + 4) = 4(x - 2)^2$.

Factor Quadratics Using Algebra Tiles

To factor quadratic expressions such as $ax^2 + bx + c$ using algebraic tiles, follow the steps :

- Model the polynomials with tiles: Start with the x^2 tiles from the upper left ensuring that the number of horizontal and vertical divisions matches the multiples of a.

- Add integer tiles in the lower right corner, with the number of horizontal and vertical divisions corresponding to integer multiples.

- Fill the remaining empty grid tiles by selecting horizontal and vertical divisions from possible multiples of a and c .

- Arrange the tiles into a rectangle grid.

- The product of expressions related to divisions: The product of the expressions associated with the horizontal divisions and vertical divisions in the grid represents the factored form of the quadratic expression.

- Check the answer.

Factoring quadratics using algebra tiles is a hands-on, visual method for understanding the factorization process. Algebra tiles are physical or virtual manipulatives that represent constants, linear terms, and quadratic terms. However, as you become more proficient in factoring, you'll likely find algebraic methods faster and more versatile.

Example:

    ✎ Use algebra tiles to factor: $x^2 - 3x + 2$

    Model the polynomials with tiles:

    In this case, arrange the tiles into a rectangle grid.

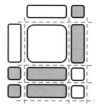

    Determine both binomials relate to the divisions, such that $x - 2$ for the horizontal division and $x - 1$ for the vertical. As follow:

    In the end, multiply two expressions and check the answer,

$$(x - 1)(x - 2) = x^2 - 3x + 2$$

Quadratic Function Vertex and Point

A quadratic function in the standard form of $y = ax^2 + bx + c$ can be transformed in the vertex form as follows:

$$y = a(x - h)^2 + k,$$

(Where (h, k) is represents the coordinate of the vertex)

So, if a is greater than $a > 0$, the function opens upward, and the vertex represents the minimum value of the function. If a is less than $a < 0$, then the function is downward, and the vertex represents the maximum value of the function.

Examples:

1) A quadratic function opening up or down has vertex $(-1, 3)$ and passes through $(2, 4)$. Write its equation in vertex form.

   Solution: Use the vertex form of the quadratic function as $y = a(x - h)^2 + k$.

   Put the coordinate of the vertex $(-1, 3)$ in the vertex form:

   $$(-1, 3) \rightarrow 3 = a\left(-1 - (-1)\right)^2 + 3 \rightarrow y = a(x + 1)^2 + 3$$

   To find a, substitute $(2, 4)$ in this equation and calculate. Then,

   $$(2, 4) \rightarrow 4 = a(2 + 1)^2 + 3 \rightarrow 4 = 9a + 3 \rightarrow 9a = 1 \rightarrow a = \frac{1}{9}.$$

   Therefore, the equation of the quadratic function in the vertex form is as follows:

   $$y = \frac{1}{9}(x + 1)^2 + 3.$$

2) A quadratic function has vertex $(-3, 4)$ and passes through $(1, -2)$. Write its equation in vertex form.

   Solution: By using the vertex form formula: $y = a(x - h)^2 + k$. So, we have:

   $$(-3, 4) \rightarrow 4 = a\left(-3 - (-3)\right)^2 + 4 \rightarrow y = a(x + 3)^2 + 4.$$

   Substitute $(1, -2)$ in the obtained equation, then:

   $$(1, -2) \rightarrow -2 = a(1 + 3)^2 + 4 \rightarrow -2 = 16a + 4 \rightarrow 16a = -6 \rightarrow 16a = -\frac{3}{8}$$

   Therefore, $y = -\frac{3}{8}(x + 3)^2 + 4$.

Chapter 7: Polynomials

 Mathematical concepts covered:

- ◉ Simplifying Polynomials
- ◉ Adding and Subtracting Polynomials
- ◉ Add and Subtract Polynomials Using Algebra Tiles
- ◉ Multiplying Monomials
- ◉ Multiplying and Dividing Monomials
- ◉ Multiplying a Polynomial and a Monomial
- ◉ Multiply Polynomials Using Area Models
- ◉ Multiplying Binomials
- ◉ Multiply two Binomials Using Algebra Tiles
- ◉ Factoring Trinomials
- ◉ Factoring Polynomials
- ◉ Use a Graph to Factor Polynomials
- ◉ Factoring Special Case Polynomials
- ◉ Add Polynomials to Find Perimeter

Simplifying Polynomials

Simplifying polynomials often involves combining like terms and arranging terms in descending order of their degree. To simplify polynomials, follow these steps:

1. Find "like" terms: Like terms are terms that have the same variables with the same powers. Group these terms together.

2. Use "FOIL". (First–Out–In–Last) for binomials:

$$(x + a)(x + b) = x^2 + (b + a)x + ab$$

3. Add or subtract "like" terms.

Examples:

1) Simplify this expression. $x(5x + 8) - 3x =$

Solution: Use Distributive Property:

$x(5x + 8) = 5x^2 + 8x$.

Now, combine like terms:

$x(5x + 8) - 3x = 5x^2 + 8x - 3x = 5x^2 + 5x$.

2) Simplify this expression. $(x + 4)(x + 3) =$

Solution: First, apply the FOIL method:

$(a + b)(c + d) = ac + ad + bc + bd$.

Therefore:

$(x + 4)(x + 3) = x^2 + 4x + 3x + 12$.

Now combine like terms:

$x^2 + 4x + 3x + 12 = x^2 + 7x + 12$.

3) Simplify this expression. $3(x^2 - 4) + 2x - 5 =$.

Solution: Use by multiplying 3 with each term inside the parentheses:

$3(x^2 - 4) = 3x^2 - 4$.

Then combine like terms:

$3x^2 - 12 + 2x - 5 = 3x^2 + 2x - 17$

Adding and Subtracting Polynomials

Adding polynomials is just a process that involves combining like terms, with some order of operations considerations thrown in.

It is important to pay attention to the signs, and don't confuse addition and multiplication!

For subtracting polynomials, sometimes you need to use the Distributive Property: $a(b + c) = ab + ac, a(b - c) = ab - ac.$

Examples:

1) Simplify the expressions. $(2x^2 - 3x) - (4x^2 + x) =$

   Solution: First, use Distributive Property: $(2x^2 - 3x) - (4x^2 + x)$.

   $\rightarrow (x^2 - 2x^3) - (x^3 - 3x^2) = x^2 - 2x^3 - x^3 + 3x^2$.

   Combine like terms: $2x^2 - 4x^2 - 3x - x = -2x^2 - 4x$.

   The simplified expression is $-2x^2 - 4x$

2) Add expressions. $(4x^3 - 2x^2) + (3x^3 + 5x^2) =$

   Solution: Remove parentheses:

   $(4x^3 - 2x^2) + (3x^3 + 5x^2) = 4x^3 2x^2 + 3x^3 + 5x^2$.

   Now combine like terms: $4x^3 + 3x^3 - 2x^2 + 5x^2 = 7x^3 + 3x^2$.

3) Simplify the expressions. $(-4x^2 - 2x^3) - (5x^2 + 2x^3) =$

   Solution: First, use Distributive Property: $-(5x^2 + 2x^3) = -5x^2 - 2x^3 \rightarrow$ $(-4x^2 - 2x^3) - (5x^2 + 2x^3) = -4x^2 - 2x^3 - 5x^2 - 2x^3$.

   Now combine like terms and write in standard form:

   $-4x^2 - 2x^3 - 5x^2 - 2x^3 = -4x^3 - 9x^2$.

4) Simplify the expressions. $(2x^2 - 5x) - (3x^2 + 2x - 1) =$

   Solution: Remove parentheses:

   $(2x^2 - 5x) - (3x^2 + 2x - 1) = 2x^2 - 5x - 3x^2 - 2x + 1$.

   Now combine like terms and write in standard form:

   $2x^2 - 5x - 3x^2 - 2x + 1 = -x^2 - 7x + 1$.

Add and Subtract Polynomials Using Algebra Tiles

To better understand and visualize the addition and subtraction of algebraic expressions, Algebra tiles can be utilized in the following manner:

- Model the polynomials using tiles.

- For algebraic subtraction, change the color of the tiles on the second side.

- Cross out the same number of negative or positive tiles on both sides of the equation.

- Write the answer by determining the number of remaining tiles.

Examples:

1) Use algebra tiles to simplify: $(x^2 - x + 3) + (2x^2 + 3x - 2)$.

   Solution: Model the given polynomials using algebra tiles.

   Here, cross out one x tile on the left side and do the same on the other side. In the same way, cancel two 1 tiles on the left side and do the same on the right side. That is,

   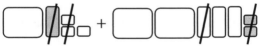

   Count the number of remaining tiles. So, $3x^2 + 2x + 1$.

2) Simplify the polynomial $(2x^2 + 3x - 1) - (x^2 - 2x - 2)$ using algebra tiles.

   Solution: Model the polynomials with tiles.

   Change the color of the tiles on the second side, then add them to the first side.

   Now, simplify the obtained algebraic tiles by canceling negative and positive tiles of the same size. As follow:

   Finally, by counting the remaining tiles, the following expression obtains: $x^2 + 5x + 1$.

Multiplying Monomials

A monomial is a polynomial with only one term: Examples: $2x$ or $7y^2$.

When multiplying monomials, you follow the following rules:

- Multiply the coefficients: a number placed before and multiplying the variable.

- Multiply the variables: and then multiply the variables using multiplication property of exponents.

$$x^a \times x^b = x^{a+b}$$

Examples:

1) Multiply expressions. $3xy^4 \times 6x^5y^3$.

   Solution: Find the same variables and use multiplication property of exponents: $x^a \times x^b = x^{a+b}$.

   $x \times x^5 = x^{1+5} = x^6$ and $y^4 \times y^3 = y^{4+3} = y^7$.

   Then, multiply coefficients and variables: $3xy^4 \times 6x^5y^3 = 18x^6y^7$.

2) Multiply expressions. $4a^3b^8 \times 2a^6b^4 =$

   Solution: Use the multiplication property of exponents: $x^a \times x^b = x^{a+b}$.

   $a^3 \times a^6 = a^{3+6} = a^9$ and $b^8 \times b^4 = b^{8+4} = b^{12}$.

   Then: $4a^3b^8 \times 2a^6b^4 = 8a^9b^{12}$.

3) Multiply. $3x^2y^4z^3 \times 5y^7z^5$

   Solution: Use the multiplication property of exponents: $x^a \times x^b = x^{a+b}$.

   $x^2 \times x^4 = x^{2+4} = x^6$, $y^4 \times y^7 = y^{4+7} = y^{11}$ and $z^3 \times z^5 = z^{3+5} = z^8$.

   Then: $3x^2y^4z^3 \times 5x^4y^7z^5 = 15x^6y^{11}z^8$.

4) Simplify. $(-6a^5b^3)(4a^8b^2) =$

   Solution: Use the multiplication property of exponents: $x^a \times x^b = x^{a+b}$.

   $a^5 \times a^8 = a^{5+8} = a^{13}$ and $b^3 \times b^2 = b^{3+2} = b^5$.

   Then: $(-6a^5b^3)(4a^8b^2) = -24a^{13}b^5$.

Multiplying and Dividing Monomials

When two monomials are divided or multiplied, you should first divide or multiply their coefficients and then divide or multiply their variables. In situations where the exponents have the same base, the following rules apply:

- For division, you subtract the powers of the exponents.
- For multiplication, you add the powers of the exponents.

Rules for multiplying and dividing exponents:

$$x^a \times x^b = x^{a+b}; \ \frac{x^a}{x^b} = x^{a-b}$$

Examples:

1) Multiply expressions. $(2x^5)(8x^4) =$

   Solution: Use multiplication property of exponents:

   $x^a \times x^b = x^{a+b} \rightarrow x^5 \times x^4 = x^9$, Then: $(2x^5)(8x^4) = 16x^9$.

   Multiply expressions. $(-3x^5)(7x^6) =$

   Solution: Use multiplication property of exponents:

   $x^a \times x^b = x^{a+b} \rightarrow x^5 \times x^6 = x^{11}$.

   Then: $(-3x^5)(7x^6) = -21x^{11}$.

2) Divide expressions. $\frac{49x^4y^6}{7xy^2} =$

   Solution: Use division property of exponents:

   $\frac{x^a}{x^b} = x^{a-b} \rightarrow \frac{x^4}{x} = x^{4-1} = x^3$ and $\frac{y^6}{y^2} = y^{6-2} = y^4$

   Then: $\frac{49x^4y^6}{7xy^2} = 7x^3y^4$.

3) Divide expressions. $\frac{81a^6b^9}{3a^3b^4}$

   Solution: Use division property of exponents:

   $\frac{x^a}{x^b} = x^{a-b} \rightarrow \frac{a^6}{a^3} = a^{6-3} = a^3$ and $\frac{b^9}{b^4} = b^{9-4} = b^5$.

   Then: $\frac{81a^6b^9}{3a^3b^4} = 27a^3b^5$.

Multiplying a Polynomial and a Monomial

Multiplying a polynomial by a monomial involves distributing the monomial to each term in the polynomial. The multiplication is carried out using the distributive property and the rules of exponents. When multiplying monomials, use the product rule for exponents.

$$x^a \times x^b = x^{a+b}$$

When multiplying a monomial by a polynomial, use the distributive property.

$$a \times (b + c) = a \times b + a \times c = ab + ac$$
$$a \times (b - c) = a \times b - a \times c = ab - ac$$

Examples:

1) Multiply the polynomial $(3x^2 - 5x + 2)$ by the monomial $(2x)$.

   A. Distribute the Monomial:

- Multiply $(2x)$ with $(3x^2)$: $(2x \times 3x^2 = 6x^{3)}$
- Multiply $(2x)$ with $(-5x)$: $(2x \times -5x = -10x^{2)}$
- Multiply $(2x)$ with (2): $(2x \times 2 = 4x)$

   B. Apply the rules of Exponents (if applicable): In the first multiplication, $(x^1 \times x^2)$ gives (x^3)

   C. Write the Resulting Terms: The resulting polynomial after multiplication is $(6x^3 - 10x^2 + 4x)$.

2) Multiply expressions. $4x(3x + 6)$

   Solution: Use Distributive Property:

   $4x(3x + 6) = 4x \times 3x + 4x \times 6 = 12x^2 + 24x$.

3) Multiply. $-x(-3x^2 + 5x + 6)$

   Solution: Use Distributive Property:

   $-x(-3x^2 + 5x + 6) = (-x) \times (-3x^2) + (-x) \times (5x) + (-x) \times (6) = 3x^3 - 5x^2 - 6x$.

4) Multiply. $-3x(-5x^2 + 3x - 6)$

   Solution: Use Distributive Property:

   $-3x(-5x^2 + 3x - 6) = (-3x) \times (-5x^2) + (-3x) \times (3x) + (-3x) \times (-6) = 15x^3 - 9x^2 + 18x$.

Multiply Polynomials Using Area Models

To multiply polynomials using area models, follow the steps:

- Model a rectangular area where each side represents one of the polynomials.
- Divide each side associated with the polynomials, separating them into their monomial factors.
- Complete the areas by multiplying the corresponding monomials together.
- To find the product of the polynomials, add up the resulting expressions from the completed areas.

Examples:

1) Use the area model to find the product $2x(x + 1)$.

   Solution: Model a rectangular area,

   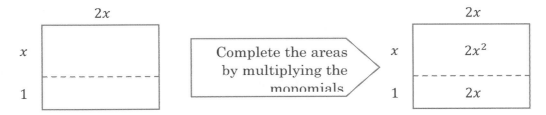

   Last, combine terms to find the polynomial product.

   $2x(x + 1) = 2x^2 + 2x$.

2) Use an area model to multiply these binomials. $(a - 2)(3a + 1)$

   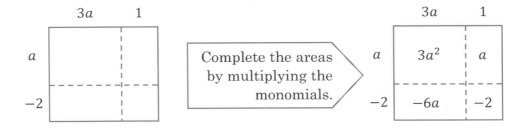

   Solution: Draw an area model representing the product $(a - 2)(3a + 1)$.

   Now, add the partial products to find the product and simplify,

   $3a^2 + a - 6a - 2 = 3a^2 - 5a - 2$.

   Therefore, $(a - 2)(3a + 1) = 3a^2 - 5a - 2$.

Multiplying Binomials

A binomial is a type of polynomial consisting of two terms, which can be either added or subtracted monomials.

To multiply two binomials, use the "FOIL" method. (First–Out–In–Last)

$$(x + a)(x + b) = x \times x + x \times b + a \times x + a \times b = x^2 + bx + ax + ab$$

Examples:

1) Multiply Binomials. $(x + 4)(x - 3) =$

   Solution: Use "FOIL". (First–Out–In–Last):

   $(x + 4)(x - 3) = x^2 - 3x + 4x - 12.$

   Then combine like terms: $x^2 - 3x + 4x - 12 = x^2 + x - 12.$

2) Multiply. $(x + 5)(x + 4) =$

   Solution: Use "FOIL". (First–Out–In–Last):

   $(x + 5)(x + 4) = x^2 + 4x + 5x + 20.$

   Then simplify: $x^2 + 4x + 5x + 20 = x^2 + 9x + 20.$

3) Multiply. $(x + 8)(x - 5) =$

   Solution: Use "FOIL". (First–Out–In–Last):

   $(x + 8)(x - 5) = x^2 - 5x + 8x - 40.$

   Then simplify: $x^2 - 5x + 8x - 40 = x^2 + 3x - 40.$

4) Multiply Binomials. $(x - 7)(x - 2) =$

   Solution: Use "FOIL". (First–Out–In–Last):

   $(x - 7)(x - 2) = x^2 - 2x - 7x + 14.$

   Then combine like terms: $x^2 - 2x - 7x + 14 = x^2 - 9x + 14.$

Multiply two Binomials Using Algebra Tiles

To determine the product of two binomials using algebraic tiles, follow these steps:

- Arrange the grid so that the horizontal divisions correspond to one of the binomials and the vertical divisions to the other side.

- Match the corresponding tiles within the grid. To obtain the result, combine the like terms within the grid.

keep these rules for performing multiplication of binomials containing a negative term:

- Multiplying two positive terms or two negative terms results in a positive value.

- Multiplying a positive term with a negative term yields a negative value.

Example:

✍ Use algebra tiles to simplify: $(x - 2)(2x + 1)$.

Solution: Set up the grid as follow:

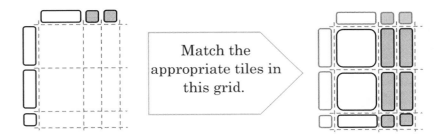

Match the appropriate tiles in this grid.

Here, cross out one x tile on the first column and do the same on the second column.

Count the like terms inside the grid. Since the number of x^2 tiles $= 2$, the number of $-x$ tiles $= 3$, and the number of -1 tiles $= 2$, then, sum the like terms inside the grid. So, $2x^2 - 3x - 2$.

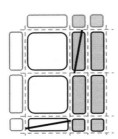

Factoring Trinomials

Factoring trinomials is a common technique in algebra. When a trinomial is factorable, it can often be expressed as the product of two binomials. To factor trinomials, you can use following methods:

- "FOIL": $(x + a)(x + b) = x^2 + (b + a)x + ab$.

- "Difference of Squares":

$$a^2 - b^2 = (a + b)(a - b)$$
$$a^2 + 2ab + b^2 = (a + b)(a + b)$$
$$a^2 - 2ab + b^2 = (a - b)(a - b)$$

- "Reverse FOIL": $x^2 + (b + a)x + ab = (x + a)(x + b)$.

Factoring trinomials can be tricky, especially when a ≠ 1 form $ax^2 + bx + c$. With practice, the process becomes more understanding, and recognizing common factors or patterns can speed up the process.

Examples:

1) Factor this trinomial. $x^2 - 6x - 27$

   Solution: to factor this trinomial, we can break it into groups. We need to find two numbers whose product is -27 and whose sum is -6. (remember "Reverse FOIL": $x^2 + (b + a)x + ab = (x + a)(x + b)$). Those two numbers are 3 and -9. Then:

   $x^2 - 6x - 27 = (x^2 + 3x) + (-9x - 27)$.

   Now factor out x from $x^2 + 3x$: $x(x + 3)$, and factor out -9 from

   $-9x - 27$: $-9(x + 3)$; Then: $(x^2 + 3x) + (-9x - 27) = x(x + 3) - 9(x + 3)$

   Now factor out like term: $(x + 3)$. Then: $(x + 3)(x - 9)$.

2) Factor this trinomial. $x^2 - 2x - 24$

   Solution: Break the expression into groups: $(x^2 + 4x) + (-6x - 24)$.

   Now factor out x from $x^2 + 4x$: $x(x + 4)$, and factor out -6 from

   $-6x - 24$: $-6(x + 4)$; Combine the factored terms: $x(x + 4) - 6(x + 4)$, now factor out like term:

   $(x + 4) \rightarrow x(x + 4) - 6(x + 4) = (x + 4)(x - 6)$.

Factoring Polynomials

To factor a polynomial:

- Step 1: Break down each term into its prime factors.

- Step 2: Find GCF (greatest common factor).

- Step 3: Factor the GCF out from each term.

- Step 4: Simplify as needed.

- To factor a polynomial, you can also use these formulas:

$$(x + a)(x + b) = x^2 + (b + a)x + ab$$
$$a^2 - b^2 = (a + b)(a - b)$$
$$a^2 + 2ab + b^2 = (a + b)(a + b)$$
$$a^2 - 2ab + b^2 = (a - b)(a - b)$$

Examples:

Factor each polynomial.

1) $7x^3 - 7x$

Solution: To factorize the expression $7x^3 - 7x$, first factor out the largest common factor, $6x$, and then you will see that you have the pattern of the difference between two complete squares: $(a - b)(a + b) = a^2 - b^2$, then: $7x^3 - 7x = 7x(x^2 - 1) = 7x(x - 1)(x + 1)$.

2) $x^2 + 9x + 20$

Solution: To factorize the expression $x^2 + 9x + 20$, you need to find two numbers whose product is 20 and sum is 9. You can get the number 20 by multiplying 1×20, 2×10, 4×5.The last pair will be your choice, because $4 + 5 = 9$. Then: $x^2 + 9x + 20 = (x + 4)(x + 5)$.

Use a Graph to Factor Polynomials

When a polynomial includes the factor of the form $(x - h)^p$, the behavior near the x −intercept can be determined by the power p. We can describe$x = h$ has a zero of multiplicity p:

- If a polynomial function graph touches the $x-$axis, at a specific $x - intercept$, it indicates that the zero at that point has an even multiplicity.

- If a polynomial function' graph crosses the $x-$axis, at a specific x-intercept, it means that the zero at that point has an odd multiplicity.

- A polynomial function' graph gets flattered at zero if the multiplicity of the zero is higher.

- When the multiplicity of a zero is higher, the polynomial function's graph becomes flatter near that zero.

- The sum of the multiplicities of all zeros is equal to the degree of the polynomial function.

To check factorization using a graphing calculator, follow these steps:

- 1st step: Press the $Y =$ button and enter the given equation for $Y1$.

- 2nd step: Press the GRAPH button to see the equation's graph.

- 3rd step: Press the TRACE button and by the left and right buttons move the cursor along the graph. You can see at which points the graph crosses the $x-$axis.

- 4th step: To find the $y-$values at the $x-$values when the graph crosses the $x-$axis, enter the value of x at this point and press ENTER button while in Trace mode. The calculator finds the $y-$value for you. The calculator tells you that in these values of x the $y-$values are equal to zero.

- 5th step: Remember that for functions with binomial factors of the form $(x - a)$, a is an $x-$intercept.

Example:

Use a graph to factor following polynomial,

$$x^2 - x - 2$$

Solution: First, graph the polynomial. Then find the points where the polynomial function graph crosses the $x-$axis. These points are the zeros of the polynomial function. For $x^2 - x - 2$, $x = -1$ and $x = 2$ are the zeros of the polynomial function.

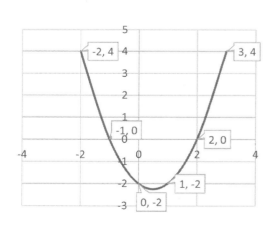

Factoring Special Case Polynomials

There are various methods for factoring special polynomials. Here are some common polynomial cases to factor:

❖ Difference of two complete squares:

$$x^2 - a^2 = (x - a)(x + a)$$

❖ Perfect square trinomial:

$$a^2 + 2ab + b^2 = (a + b)^2$$

$$a^2 - 2ab + b^2 = (a - b)^2$$

❖ FOIL (First, Outer, Inner, Last):

$$(x + a)(x + b) = x^2 + (a + b)x + ab$$

❖ Reverse FOIL:

$$x^2 + (a + b)x + ab = (x + a)(x + b)$$

❖ Sum of Cubes: For any real numbers a and b:

$$a^3 + b^3 = (a + b)(a^2 - ab + b^2)$$

Understanding and recognizing these patterns is beneficial when trying to factor certain polynomial expressions. As with all algebraic skills, the more you practice identifying and factoring these special case polynomials, the easier it will become.

Examples:

1) Factor completely. $49y^2 + 28y + 4$

   Solution: You may notice that two terms $49y^2$ and 4 are perfect squares. The root $49y^2$ is equal to $7y$, and the root 4 is equal to 2. The middle expression, $28y$, is equal to twice the product of $7y$ and 2. So, you have a perfect square trinomial whose factoring result is $(7y + 2)^2$. $25y^2 + 28y + 9 = (7y + 2)^2$.

2) Factor completely. $49y^2 - 36x^4$

   Solution: Phrase $49y^2$ can be written in form $(7y)^2$ and phrase $36x^4$ in form $(6x^2)^2$. Therefore, the relation of the question form is as follows:
   $(7y)^2 - (6x^2)^2 = (7y - 6x^2)(7y + 6x^2)$.

Add Polynomials to Find Perimeter

To find the perimeter of a two-dimensional shape with sides represented by polynomials, you simply combining like terms that represent equivalent lengths or distances.

Examples:

1) Find the perimeter. Simplify your answer.

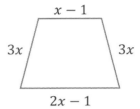

Solution: The perimeter of the shape is the sum of the sides. So,

Perimeter $= (x - 1) + (3x) + (2x - 1) + (3x)$

$= x - 1 + 3x + 2x - 1 + 3x.$

Group and add like terms,

Perimeter $= (x + 3x + 2x + 3x) + (-1 - 1) = 9x - 2.$

2) What is the perimeter of the rectangle if the length is $4x^2 - 2$ and the width is $8x + 4$?

Solution: The perimeter of the rectangle is,

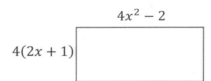

Perimeter $= 2\big((4x^2 - 2) + 4(2x + 1)\big)$

Expand the expression and simplify,

Perimeter $= 2\big((4x^2 - 2) + (8x + 4)\big)$

$= 2(4x^2 - 2 + 8x + 4)$

$= 2(4x^2 + 8x + 2)$

$= 8x^2 + 16x + 4.$

Chapter 8 :
Functions

 Mathematical concepts covered:

- ◉ Relation and Functions
- ◉ Complete a Function Table
- ◉ Domain and Range of Relations
- ◉ Rate of Change and Slope
- ◉ Function Notation and Evaluation
- ◉ Adding and Subtracting Functions
- ◉ Multiplying and Dividing Functions
- ◉ Composition of Functions
- ◉ Evaluate an Exponential Function
- ◉ Match Exponential Functions and Graphs
- ◉ Exponential Functions Word Problems
- ◉ Function Inverses

Relation and Functions

"Relation" and "function" are fundamental concepts in algebra and calculus.

Relation: A relation is simply a set of ordered pairs. It relates elements from one set, called the domain, to another set, called the codomain.

✓ If we have the relation ($R = \{(1,2),(2,3),(3,4)\}$), it relates each element from the set of first components (domain) to the set of second components (range).

✓ A relation can be represented in various ways: as a set of ordered pairs, a table, a graph, or a mapping.

Function: A function is a special type of relation where every element in the domain is related to exactly one element in the range.

✓ For a relation to be a function, each input (or "x-value") can only be paired with one unique output (or "y-value").

✓ A common notation for functions is ($f(x)$), where (f) is the name of the function and (x) is the input value. The output is represented by ($f(x)$).

✓ A function can be represented using an equation, a graph, a table, or a mapping diagram.

✓ A vertical line test on a graph can be used to determine if a relation is a function: if any vertical line intersects the graph at more than one point, the relation is not a function.

Relationship Between Relation and Function:

Every function is a relation, but not every relation is a function. The defining feature of a function is its uniqueness constraint on outputs for each input.

Examples:

- The set ($R = \{(1,2),(2,3),(3,4)\}$) is both a relation and a function.

- The set ($S = \{(1,2),(2,3),(2,4)\}$) is a relation, but it's not a function because the input 2 is related to both 3 and 4, violating the "one input, one output" rule of functions.

- The function ($f(x) = x + 1$) relates each number (x) to a number that is one greater.

Complete a Function Table

A function table, often simply called a "table of values," is a graphical representation of a function's input-output relationship. It's composed of two columns (rows): one for input values (x) and one for output values (y or $f(x)$).

To represent a relationship in mathematics, one common method is to use a function table. The function table displays the input and output values of a given equation or function.

To complete a function table for a specific equation, we follow these steps:

Step 1: Determine the input values to be included in the table. These are typically listed in the first column.

Step 2: Substitute each input value into the equation or function.

Step 3: Evaluate the output of equation.

Function tables are tools for understanding, predicting, and graphing functions.

Example:

✑ Complete the table.

$f(x) = 3x - 2$			
x	-2	0	1
$f(x)$			

Look at the function table. Clearly, the first value of the input in the table is -2.

Evaluate f$(x) = 3x - 2$ or $x = -2$.

$f(-2) = 3(-2) - 2 = -6 - 2 = -8$.

When $x = -2$, then f$(-2) = -8$.

Complete the first row of the table.

Similarly, evaluate $f(x) = 3x - 2$ for $x = 0$ and $x = 1$, respectively.

$f(x) = 3x - 2$			
x	-2	0	1
$f(x)$	-8	-2	1

So,

$f(0) = 3(0) - 2 = 0 - 2 = -2$,

$f(1) = 3(1) - 2 = 3 - 2 = 1$.

Enter the obtained values in the table.

Domain and Range of Relations

A relation is defined as a set or collection of ordered pairs that establishes a connection between elements from two sets. The ordered pairs represent the input and output values in the relationship.

The domain of a relation or function refers to the set of all input or independent values that are used as inputs for the relation or function. On the other hand, the range represents the set of all output or dependent values that result from the relation or function.

A function is a specific type of relation where each input value is uniquely connected to an output value. In other words, in a function, two different input values cannot be linked to the same output value, but the same output value can be connected to multiple input values.

When representing a function graphically, the $x-$ coordinates on the graph correspond to the domain values, while the $y-coordinates$ represent the range values.

Examples:

1) What is the domain and range of the following relation: $\{(5,1), (-2,3), (3,-1), (6,2), (7,5)\}$?

   The domain contains $x-$values of a relation and the range includes $y-$values of a relationship. So, Domain $= \{5, -2, 3, 6, 7\}$ and Range $= \{1, 3, -1, 2, 5\}$.

2) Find the domain and range of the following relation:

$$R = \{4x + 2, x - 1\}: x \in \{-2, -1, 0, 1, 2\}$$

   In the question we have given $x = \{-2, -1, 0, 1, 2\}$ Therefore, the domain of the relation R is $\{-1, -2, 0, 1, 2\}$. So, put these values into equations of $R = R = \{4x + 2, x - 1\}$ to find the range of the relation:

   $x = -2: x - 1 = -2 - 1 = -3$ $x = 1: x - 1 = 1 - 1 = 0$

   $x = -1: x - 1 = -1 - 1 = -2$ $x = 2: x - 1 = 2 - 1 = 1$

   $x = 0: x - 1 = 0 - 1 = -1$

   From these calculations, we can determine that the range of the relation R is $\{-3, -2, -1, 0, 1\}$.

Rate of Change and Slope

The rate of change is a ratio that compares the change in y-values to the change in x-values. The y-values are considered as the dependent variables, while the x-values are considered as the independent variables. In the case of a constant and linear rate of change, it corresponds to the slope of a line.

The slope of a line can be positive, negative, zero, or undefined, and it describes the direction and steepness of the line. A rising line from left to right indicates a positive slope, while a falling line from left to right indicates a negative slope. A horizontal line indicates no change and therefore has a slope of zero. A vertical line, on the other hand, is not a function and has an undefined slope because there are multiple y-values for a single x-value.

The variable m is the sign for the slope of a line. It is stated by the ratio of the subtraction of y −variables to the subtraction of x −variables. It means if $(x_1, y_1), (x_2, y_2)$ are the coordinates of 2 points on a line, then $m = \frac{y_2 - y_1}{x_2 - x_1}$.

Example:

✎ The following table shows the number of cars sold by a company in different years. Find the rate of change in car sales for each time interval. Determine which time interval has the greatest rate.

Year	2001	2006	2011	2016	2018
Number of sold cars	30	55	60	80	100

First, years are independent variables and the number of sold cars are dependent variables. Now find the rate of changes:

2001 to 2006 → m $= \frac{change\ in\ the\ number\ of\ sold\ cars}{change\ in\ years} = \frac{55-30}{2006-2001} = \frac{25}{5} = 5.$

2006 to 2011 → m $= \frac{change\ in\ the\ number\ of\ sold\ cars}{change\ in\ years} = \frac{60-55}{2011-2006} = \frac{15}{5} = 3.$

2011 to 2016 → m $= \frac{change\ in\ the\ number\ of\ sold\ cars}{change\ in\ years} = \frac{80-60}{2016-2011} = \frac{20}{5} = 4.$

2016 to 2018 → m $= \frac{change\ in\ the\ number\ of\ sold\ cars}{change\ in\ years} = \frac{100-80}{2018-2016} = \frac{20}{2} = 10.$

The greatest rate of change occurs from 2016 to 2018, with a rate of 10. This indicates that during this time interval, the number of cars sold increased at the highest rate compared to the other intervals.

Function Notation and Evaluation

Functions are mathematical operations that assign unique outputs to given inputs. Function notation is a short way of representing a function.

The most popular function notation is $f(x)$ which is read "f of x". Any letter can name a function. for example: $g(x)$, $h(x)$, etc.

To evaluate a function, substitute the given value or expression into the function's variable, usually denoted by "x," and calculate the corresponding output.

Advantages of Function Notation:

- **Clarity:** Function notation clearly indicates which variable is the input, and what rule should be applied to it.

- **Flexibility**: We can easily work with multiple functions in the same problem without confusing their rules or variables.

- **Expression of Relationships**: It emphasizes that the output value is dependent on the input value. The value of f(x) changes as x changes.

Function notation provides a standardized way to communicate about and work with functions.

Examples:

1) Evaluate: $f(x) = x + 8$, find $f(3)$

Substitute x with 3: Then: $f(x) = x + 8 \rightarrow f(3) = 3 + 8 \rightarrow f(3) = 11$.

2) Evaluate: $g(x) = 4x - 1$, find $g(-2)$.

Substitute x with -2:

Then: $g(x) = 4x - 1 \rightarrow g(-2) = 4(-2) - 1 = -8 - 1 = -9$.

3) Evaluate: $f(x) = 4x^2 + 8$, find $f(0)$.

Solution: Substitute x with 0:

Then: $f(x) = 4x^2 + 8 \rightarrow f(0) = 4(0)^2 + 8 \rightarrow f(0) = 8$.

4) Evaluate: $h(x) = 3x^2 - 9$, find $h(2a)$.

Solution: Substitute x with $2a$:

Then: $h(x) = 3x^2 - 9 \rightarrow h(2a) = 3(2a)^2 - 9 \rightarrow h(2a) = 16a^2 - 9$

Adding and Subtracting Functions

Like adding and subtracting numbers and expressions, we can also add or subtract functions and simplify or evaluate them. Adding and subtracting functions is essentially an exercise in combining like terms. As with most algebraic operations, it's crucial to carefully line up terms with the same variables and powers and then perform the arithmetic. The outcome the result is a new function.

For two functions $f(x)$ and $g(x)$, we can create two new functions:

- $(f + g)(x) = f(x) + g(x)$

- $(f - g)(x) = f(x) - g(x)$

Examples:

1) $g(x) = 3x - 3$, $f(x) = x + 2$, Find: $(g + f)(x)$.

Solution: $(g + f)(x) = g(x) + f(x)$

Then: $(g + f)(x) = (3x - 3) + (x + 2) = 3x - 3 + x + 2 = 4x - 1$.

2) $f(x) = 3x - 2$, $g(x) = 4x - 5$, Find: $(f - g)(x)$.

Solution: $(f - g)(x) = f(x) - g(x)$

Then: $(f - g)(x) = (3x - 2) - (4x - 5) = 3x - 2 - 4x + 5 = -x + 3$.

3) $g(x) = x^2 + 4$, $f(x) = x + 3$, Find: $(g + f)(x)$.

Solution: $(g + f)(x) = g(x) + f(x)$

Then: $(g + f)(x) = (x^2 + 4) + (x + 3) = x^2 + x + 7$.

4) $f(x) = 7x^2 - 5$, $g(x) = 4x + 8$, Find: $(f - g)(2)$

Solution: $(f - g)(x) = f(x) - g(x)$

Then: $(f - g)(x) = (7x^2 - 5) - (4x + 8)$

$= 7x^2 - 5 - 4x - 8 = 7x^2 - 4x - 13$.

Substitute x with 3: $(f - g)(2) = 7(2)^2 - 4(2) - 13 = 28 - 8 - 13 = 7$.

5) $g(x) = x^2 - 2$, $f(x) = 2x + 3$, Find: $(g + f)(x)$.

Solution: $(g + f)(x) = g(x) + f(x)$

Then: $(g + f)(x) = (x^2 - 2) + (2x + 3) = x^2 - 2 + 2x + 3 = x^2 + 2x + 1$.

Multiplying and Dividing Functions

Just as we can perform multiplication and division with numbers and expressions, we can also multiply and divide two functions and simplify or evaluate them.

For two functions $f(x)$ and $g(x)$, we can create two new functions:

- $(f \times g)(x) = f(x) \times g(x)$
- $\left(\dfrac{f}{g}\right)(x) = \dfrac{f(x)}{g(x)}$

Domain Restrictions: When dividing functions, you need to consider where the denominator $g(x)$ is zero. These are the values of x that are excluded from the domain of the quotient function because division by zero is undefined.

Simplification: After multiplying or dividing, always look for opportunities to simplify the resulting function.

Examples:

1) $g(x) = 2x + 3$, $f(x) = 4x - 5$, Find: $(g.f)(x)$.

   $(g.f)(x) = g(x).f(x) = (2x + 3)(4x - 5) = 8x^2 - 10x + 12x - 15$

   $= 8x^2 + 2x - 15$.

2) $f(x) = x + 7$, $h(x) = x - 10$, Find: $\left(\dfrac{f}{h}\right)(x)$.

   Solution: $\left(\dfrac{f}{h}\right)(x) = \dfrac{f(x)}{h(x)} = \dfrac{x+7}{x-10}$.

3) $g(x) = x + 7$, $f(x) = x - 3$, Find: $(g.f)(2)$.

   Solution: $(g.f)(x) = g(x).f(x) = (x + 7)(x - 3) = x^2 - 3x + 7x - 21$.

   Then: $g(x).f(x) = x^2 + 4x - 21$.

   Substitute x with 2: $(g.f)(2) = (2)^2 + 4(2) - 21 = 4 + 8 - 21 = -9$.

4) $f(x) = x + 2$, $h(x) = 2x - 6$, Find: $\left(\dfrac{f}{h}\right)(4)$.

   Solution: $\left(\dfrac{f}{h}\right)(x) = \dfrac{f(x)}{h(x)} = \dfrac{x+2}{2x-6}$.

   Substitute x with 4: $\left(\dfrac{f}{h}\right)(4) = \dfrac{4+2}{2(4)-6} = \dfrac{6}{2} = 3$.

5) $g(x) = x + 7$, $f(x) = x - 3$, Find: $(g.f)(2)$.

   Solution: $(g.f)(x) = g(x).f(x) = (x + 7)(x - 3) = x^2 + 2x - 21$.

   Substitute x with 2: $(g.f)(2) = (2)^2 + 2(2) - 21 = 4 + 4 - 21 = -13$.

Composition of Functions

Composition of functions involves combining two or more functions in a way that the output of one function becomes the input for the next function.

The notation used for composition is: $(fog)(x) = f(g(x))$ and is read "f composed with g of x" or "f of g of x".

- It's important to note that in general, $f \circ g$ is not necessarily equal to $g \circ f$.

Identity Function: For any function f, there exists an identity function I such that: $f \circ I = I \circ f$ Where $I(x) = x$.

Examples:

1) Using $f(x) = 3x + 2$ and $g(x) = 4x$, find: $(fog)(x)$.

   Solution: $(fog)(x) = f(g(x))$. Then:

   $(fog)(x) = f(g(x)) = f(5x)$.

   Now find $f(4x)$ by substituting x with $4x$ in $f(x)$ function.

   Then:

   $f(x) = 3x + 2; (x \to 4x) \to f(4x) = 3(4x) + 2 = 12x + 2$.

2) Using $f(x) = 5x - 2$ and $g(x) = 3x - 1$, find: $(gof)(3)$.

   Solution: $(fog)(x) = f(g(x))$. Then:

   $(gof)(x) = g(f(x)) = g(5x - 2)$,

   Now substitute x in $g(x)$ by $(5x - 2)$.

   Then:

   $g(5x - 2) = 3(5x - 2) - 1 = 15x - 6 - 1 = 15x - 7$.

   Substitute x with 5: $(gof)(3) = g(f(3)) = 15(3) - 7 = 45 - 7 = 38$.

3) Using $f(x) = 2x^2 - 3$ and $g(x) = x + 4$, find: $f(g(2))$.

   Solution: First, find $g(2)$:

   $g(x) = x + 4 \to g(2) = 2 + 4 = 6$.

   Then: $f(g(2)) = f(6)$.

   Now, find $f(6)$ by substituting x with 6 in $f(x)$ function.

   $f(g(2)) = f(6) = 2(6)^2 - 3 = 2(36) - 3 = 69$.

Evaluate an Exponential Function

An exponential function is an equation of the form $f(x) = ab^x$, where a is a non-zero real number and b is a positive real number. This function applies to any real number x.

To evaluate an exponential function, you'll substitute a given input for the independent variable (x) into the function and do the calculation to find the output value.

- If working with a calculator, use the exponential or power function button to compute the value.

- Exponential functions model various real-life situations, from population growth, radioactive decay, to interest accumulation in finance. Understanding how to evaluate them lets us make predictions about them.

- When working with exponential functions, always be cautious of the base. Recognizing whether the function represents growth or decay.

Examples:

1) Let $f(x) = 2^x$. What is $f(3)$?

   To evaluate $f(3)$, plug 3 in the equation $f(x) = 2^x$

   So, $f(3) = 2^3 = 8$.

2) Use the following function to find $f(4)$.

$$f(x) = -3(2)^{\frac{x}{2}-1}$$

   First, substitute $x = 4$ in the equation,

$$f(4) = -3(2)^{\frac{4}{2}-1} = -3(2)^{2-1} = -3(2) = -6$$

3) Use the following function to find $f(2)$.

$$f(x) = 4\left(\frac{1}{2}\right)^{2x-1} + 1$$

   Solution: To solve, plug 4 into $f(x) = 4\left(\frac{1}{2}\right)^{2x-1} + 1$ instead of x. So,

$$f(2) = 4\left(\frac{1}{2}\right)^{2(2)-1} + 1 = 4\left(\frac{1}{2}\right)^{4-1} + 1 = 4\left(\frac{1}{2}\right)^3 + 1$$

$$= 4\left(\frac{1}{8}\right) + 1 = \frac{1}{2} + 1 = \frac{3}{2}.$$

Match Exponential Functions and Graphs

To match an exponential function $y = b^x$ with its corresponding graph and vice versa, you can follow these steps:

Examine the relationship of growth or decay:

- If $b > 1$, the function is growing.

- If $0 < b < 1$, the function is decaying.

Evaluate the value of the function at a few inputs to match some points on the graph, like the $y-$intercept.

Determine the end behavior of the function.

Example:

 Match each exponential function to its graph.

$$f(x) = \left(\frac{1}{2}\right)^x, g(x) = \left(\frac{3}{2}\right)^x h(x) = \left(\frac{1}{3}\right)^x$$

A

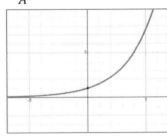

B

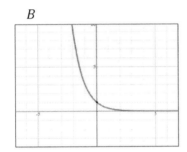

C

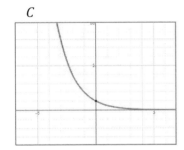

According to the base value of the exponential equation, notice that one of the functions is growing and the other two functions are decaying. So, the function $g(x) = \left(\frac{3}{2}\right)^x$ can be equivalent to graph A. Now, evaluate the two remaining functions at a few inputs to find some points on the graph. Choose a point such as -1 to plug into the equation. Therefore, start with $f(x) = \left(\frac{1}{2}\right)^x$.

$$f(-1) = \left(\frac{1}{2}\right)^{-1} = 2.$$

You can see that the ordered pair $(-1,2)$ for the function $f(x) = \left(\frac{1}{2}\right)^x$ is equivalent to a point on graph C. In the same way, substitute -1 in $h(x) = \left(\frac{1}{3}\right)^x$.

Therefore, $h(-1) = \left(\frac{1}{3}\right)^{-1} = 3$. That is, graph B represented the function $h(x)$.

Exponential Functions Word Problems

To solve word problems involving exponential functions, follow these steps:

Step 1: Check that it changes at the constant ratio.

Step 2: Identify the given values such as the ratio and the initial amount provided in the problem.

Step 3: Substitute the given values into the exponential formula.

Step 4: Evaluate the requested values.

Examples:

1) In a laboratory sample, if it starts with 200 bacteria which can double every hour, how many bacteria will there be after 3 hours?

   Solution: Since the bacteria population doubles every hour, we can use the exponential formula to determine the number of bacteria. Let's use the formula:

   $$y = ab^n$$

   Where a is the initial number of bacteria (200) and b is the constant ratio (2). Substituting these values into the formula, we have: $y = 200(2)^n$

   To find the number of bacteria after 3 hours, we plug in n = 3:

   $$y = 200(2)^3 = 200(8) = 1,600.$$

   Therefore, after 3 hours, there will be 1600 bacteria in the laboratory sample.

2) A computer model is priced at $1,800 and depreciates in value by 15% each year. Write an equation that represents the value of the computer model at the year. How much will the computer model be worth in 5 years?

   Solution: To write the equation for the value of the computer model at the year, we can use the exponential equation: $y = ab^x$, where a is the initial amount and b is the ratio of changes. In this case, the change ratio is obtained as $b = (1 - r)$, where r is the percentage of the depreciation rate (negative).

   The initial cost of the computer model is $1,800, so the equation becomes:

   $$y = 18,000(0.85)^t$$

   To find the value of the computer model after 5 years, we substitute t = 5 into the equation: $y = 18,000(0.85)^5 \cong 18,000(0.4437) \cong 799.26.$

Function Inverses

An inverse function is a function that undoes or reverses the effect of another function. if the function f takes an input x gives a result of y, then the inverse function g, when applied to y, returns the original input x.

$f(x) = y$ if and only if $g(y) = x$.

The inverse function of $f(x)$ is usually shown by $f^{-1}(x)$.

Examples:

1) Find the inverse of the function: $f(x) = 2x + 5$.

   Solution: First, replace $f(x)$ with y: $y = 2x + 5$. Then, replace all x's with y and all y's with x: $x = 2y + 5$.

   Now, solve for y: $x = 2y + 5 \rightarrow x - 5 = 2y \rightarrow \frac{1}{2}x - \frac{5}{2} = y$.

   Finally replace y with $f^{-1}(x)$:

   $f^{-1}(x) = \frac{1}{2}x - \frac{5}{2}$.

4) Find the inverse of the function: $g(x) = \frac{1}{7}x + 2$.

   Solution: $g(x) = \frac{1}{7}x + 2 \rightarrow y = \frac{1}{7}x + 2$,

   replace all x's with y and all y's with x; $x = \frac{1}{7}y + 2$,

   solve for y:

   $x - 2 = \frac{1}{7}y \rightarrow 7(x - 2) = y \rightarrow g^{-1}(x) = 7x - 14$.

5) Find the inverse of the function: $h(x) = \sqrt{x} + 5$.

   Solution: $h(x) = \sqrt{x} + 5 \rightarrow y = \sqrt{x} + 5$,

   replace all x's with y and all y's with x;

   $x = \sqrt{y} + 5 \rightarrow x - 5 = \sqrt{y} \rightarrow (x - 5)^2 = \left(\sqrt{y}\right)^2 \rightarrow x^2 - 10x + 25 = y$.

   Then:

   $h^{-1}(x) = x^2 - 10x + 25$.

Chapter 9: Rational Expressions

 Mathematical concepts covered:

- Adding and Subtracting Radical Expressions
- Multiplying Radical Expressions
- Simplifying Radical Expressions
- Rationalizing Radical Expressions
- Radical Equations
- Domain and Range of Radical Functions
- Simplify Radicals with Fractions
- Finding Distance of Two Points

Adding and Subtracting Rational Expressions

Adding and subtracting rational expressions is like adding and subtracting fractions. For adding and subtracting rational expressions:

- Find the least common denominator (LCD).

- Write each expression using the LCD.

- Add or subtract the numerators.

- Simplify as needed.

Examples:

1) Solve $\frac{5}{3x+2} + \frac{2x-3}{3x+2}$.

   Solution: The denominators are equal. Then, use fractions addition rule:

   $\frac{a}{c} \pm \frac{b}{c} = \frac{a \pm b}{c}$.

   Therefore: $\frac{5}{3x+2} + \frac{2x-3}{3x+2} = \frac{5+2x-3}{3x+2} = \frac{2x+2}{3x+2}$.

2) Solve $\frac{x+3}{x-4} + \frac{x-3}{x+5}$.

   Solution: Find the least common denominator of $(x-4)$ and $(x+5)$:

   $(x-4)(x+5)$. Then:

   $\frac{x+3}{x-4} + \frac{x-3}{x+5} = \frac{(x+3)(x+5)}{(x-4)(x+5)} + \frac{(x-3)(x-4)}{(x-4)(x+5)} = \frac{(x+3)(x+5)+(x-3)(x-4)}{(x-4)(x+5)}$.

   Expand:

   $(x+3)(x+5) + (x-3)(x-4) = 2x^2 + x + 27$.

   Then: $\frac{(x+3)(x+5)+(x-3)(x-4)}{(x-4)(x+5)} . = \frac{2x^2+x+27}{(x-4)(x+5)} = \frac{2x^2+x+27}{x^2-x-20}$.

3) Add the rational expressions: $\frac{2x}{x^2-9} + \frac{3}{x-3}$.

   The denominators are $x^2 - 9$ and $x - 3$. The LCD is $x^2 - 9$ because:

   $x^2 - 9 = (x+3)(x-3)$ So, the second fraction needs to be multiplied by $(x + 3)$ in both the numerator and the denominator to get the LCD.

   $\frac{2x}{x^2-9} + \frac{3(x+3)}{x^2-9} = \frac{2x+3x+9}{x^2-9} = \frac{5x+9}{x^2-9}$

Multiplying and Dividing Rational Expressions

Multiplying rational expressions is the same as multiplying fractions. First, Multiply the Numerators with Numerators and Denominators with Denominators($\frac{a}{b} \times \frac{c}{d} = \frac{a \times c}{b \times d}$). Then simplify as needed.

To divide rational expressions, you can apply the same method used for dividing fractions. (Keep, Change, Flip) $\frac{a}{b} \div \frac{c}{d} = \frac{a}{b} \times \frac{d}{c} = \frac{a \times d}{b \times c}$:

a) Keep the first rational expression as it is.

b) Change the division sign to multiplication.

c) Flip the numerator and denominator of the second rational expression.

d) Multiply the numerators together and multiply the denominators together.

e) Simplify the resulting expression as needed.

Examples:

1) Solve: $\frac{x-2}{x+3} \times \frac{2x+6}{x-2}$

Multiply numerators and denominators: $\frac{x-2}{x+3} \times \frac{2x+6}{x-2} = \frac{(x-2)(2x+6)}{(x+3)(x-2)}$.

Cancel the common factor: $\frac{(x-2)(2x+6)}{(x+3)(x-2)} = \frac{(2x+6)}{(x+3)}$.

Factor $2x + 6 = 2(x + 3)$. Then: $\frac{2(x+3)}{(x+3)} = 2$.

2) Solve. $\frac{2x + 3}{4x} \div \frac{x^2+7x+12}{4x^2+4x} =$

Solution: Use fractions division rule:

Therefore:

$\frac{2x + 3}{4x} \div \frac{x^2+7x+12}{4x^2+4x} = \frac{2x + 3}{4x} \times \frac{4x^2+4x}{x^2+7x+12}$.

Now, factorize the expressions $4x^2 + 4x$ and $x^2 + 7x + 12$. Then:

$4x^2 + 4x = 4x(x + 1)$ and $x^2 + 7x + 12 = (x + 3)(x + 4)$.

Simplify: $\frac{(2x + 3)(4x^2+4x)}{(4x)(x^2+7x+12)} = \frac{(2x + 3)4x(x+1)}{(4x)(x+3)(x+4)}$,

cancel common factors. Then: $\frac{(2x + 3)4x(x+1)}{(4x)(x+3)(x+4)} = \frac{(2x + 3)(x+1)}{(x+3)(x+4)}$.

Simplifying Complex Fractions

Complex fractions are fractions where the numerator, the denominator, or both contain fractions.

a) Convert mixed numbers to improper fractions by multiplying the whole number by the denominator and adding the numerator.

b) Simplify the fraction, if possible, by finding the greatest common divisor (GCD) of the numerator and denominator, then divide both the numerator and denominator by the GCD.

c) Write the fraction in the numerator of the main fraction line then write division sign ($\div$) and the fraction of the denominator.

d) Use the rules for dividing fractions: Keep, Change, Flip (Keep the first fraction, Change the division sign to multiplication, Flip the second fraction).

e) Simplify the resulting fraction as needed.

Examples:

1) Simplify: $\dfrac{\frac{7}{10}}{\frac{3}{20}-\frac{1}{5}}$.

Solution: First, simplify the denominator: $\frac{3}{20}-\frac{1}{5}=-\frac{1}{20}$, Then: $\dfrac{\frac{7}{10}}{\frac{3}{20}-\frac{1}{5}}=\dfrac{\frac{7}{10}}{-\frac{1}{20}}$.

Now, write the complex fraction using the division sign ($\div$): $\dfrac{\frac{7}{10}}{-\frac{1}{20}}=\frac{7}{10}\div\left(-\frac{1}{20}\right)$.

Dividing fractions rule (Keep, Change, Flip): $\frac{7}{10}\div\left(-\frac{1}{20}\right)=\frac{7}{10}\times-\frac{20}{1}=-\frac{140}{10}$.

Therefore, the simplified form of $-\frac{140}{10}$ is -14

2) Simplify: $\dfrac{\frac{3}{5}\div\frac{2}{3}}{\frac{4}{7}+\frac{1}{3}}$.

Solution: Step 1: Simplify the numerator: $\frac{3}{5}\div\frac{2}{3}=\frac{3}{5}\times\frac{3}{2}=\frac{9}{10}$

Step 2: Simplify the denominator: $\frac{4}{7}+\frac{1}{3}=\frac{12}{21}+\frac{7}{21}=\frac{19}{21}$

Step 3: Write the complex fraction using the division sign ($\div$): $\dfrac{\frac{3}{5}\div\frac{2}{3}}{\frac{4}{7}+\frac{1}{3}}=\dfrac{\frac{9}{10}}{\frac{19}{21}}$

Step 4: Use the dividing fractions rule (Keep, Change, Flip): $\dfrac{\frac{9}{10}}{\frac{19}{21}}=\frac{9}{10}\times\frac{21}{19}=\frac{189}{190}$

Therefore, the simplified form of $\frac{189}{190}$ is $\frac{189}{190}$

Graphing Rational Functions

A rational expression is a fraction in which the numerator and/or the denominator are polynomials. Here are some examples: $\frac{1}{x}, \frac{x^2}{x-1}, \frac{x^2-x+2}{x^2+5x+1}, \frac{m^2+6m-5}{m-2m}$.

To graph a rational, follow these steps:

- Find the vertical asymptotes of the function if any. (Vertical asymptotes are vertical lines that correspond to the zeroes of the denominator. The graph will have a vertical asymptote at $x = a$ if the denominator is zero at $x = a$ and the numerator isn't zero at $x = a$.)

- Find the horizontal or slant asymptote. If the numerator has a higher degree than the denominator, there will be a slant asymptote. To find the slant asymptote, divide the numerator by the denominator using either long division or synthetic division. If the denominator has a higher degree than the numerator, the horizontal asymptote is the $x - axis$ or the line $y = 0$. If they have the same degree, the horizontal asymptote is equal to the leading coefficient (the coefficient of the largest exponent) of the numerator divided by the leading coefficient of the denominator.

- Find intercepts and plug in some values of x and solve for y, then graph the function.

Example:

✎ Graph rational function. $f(x) = \frac{x^2-x+2}{x-1}$

First, notice that the graph is in two pieces. Most rational functions have graphs in multiple pieces. Find $y-$intercept by substituting zero for x and solving for y, $(f(x))$:

$x = 0 \rightarrow y = \frac{x^2-x+2}{x-1} = \frac{0^2-0+2}{0-1} = -2$,

$y-$intercept: $(0, -2)$

Asymptotes of $\frac{x^2-x+2}{x-1}$: Vertical: $x = 1$, Slant asymptote: $y = x$.

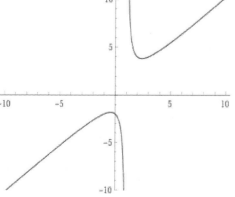

After finding the asymptotes, you can plug in some values for x and solve for y. Here is the sketch for this function.

Evaluate Integers Raised to Rational Exponents

To evaluate the rational exponents of integers, follow these steps:

- Step 1: Write the base in exponential notations.
- Step 2: Multiply the exponents obtained and simplify the result.

Examples:

1) Evaluate $64^{\frac{2}{3}}$.

   Solution: First, rewrite the base as exponential form $64 = 4^3$. Now, we have:

   $64^{\frac{2}{3}} = (4^3)^{\frac{2}{3}}$.

   So, multiply two exponents, $(4^3)^{\frac{2}{3}} = 4^{3\times\frac{2}{3}} = 4^2 = 16$.

2) Simplify $(-125)^{-\frac{1}{3}}$.

   Solution: Write the base in exponential notation, $125 = 5^3$. Then:

   $(-125)^{-\frac{1}{3}} = (-5^3)^{-\frac{1}{3}}$.

   Use this formula $a^{-b} = \frac{1}{a^b}$, so: $(-5^3)^{-\frac{1}{3}} = \frac{1}{(-5^3)^{\frac{1}{3}}} = \frac{1}{(-5)^{3\times\frac{1}{3}}} = -\frac{1}{5}$.

3) Calculate the value of $\sqrt[3]{144^{\frac{3}{2}}}$.

   Solution: Use this formula $\sqrt[n]{a} = a^{\frac{1}{n}}$. Then:

   $\sqrt[3]{144^{\frac{3}{2}}} = \left(144^{\frac{3}{2}}\right)^{\frac{1}{3}}$.

   Now, by using $(a^n)^m = a^{nm}$. So, we have: $\left(144^{\frac{3}{2}}\right)^{\frac{1}{3}} = 144^{\frac{3}{2}\times\frac{1}{3}} = 144^{\frac{1}{2}}$.

   Write the base in exponential notation, $144^{\frac{1}{2}} = (12^2)^{\frac{1}{2}}$. Multiply the exponents and simplify: $(12^2)^{\frac{1}{2}} = 12^{2\times\frac{1}{2}} = 12$.

Chapter 10: Radical Expressions

 Mathematical concepts covered:

- ⊙ Simplifying Radical Expressions
- ⊙ Adding and Subtracting Radical Expressions
- ⊙ Multiplying Radical Expressions
- ⊙ Rationalizing Radical Expressions
- ⊙ Radical Equations
- ⊙ Domain and Range of Radical Functions
- ⊙ Simplify Radicals with Fractions
- ⊙ Finding Distance of Two Points

Simplifying Radical Expressions

Follow these steps to simplify them:

- Find the prime factors of the numbers or expressions inside the radical.

- Use radical properties to simplify the radical expression. The following properties can be used:

  - $\sqrt[n]{x^a} = x^{\frac{a}{n}},$
  - $\sqrt[n]{xy} = x^{\frac{1}{n}} \times y^{\frac{1}{n}}$

  - $\sqrt[n]{\frac{x}{y}} = \frac{x^{\frac{1}{n}}}{y^{\frac{1}{n}}}$
  - $\sqrt[n]{x} \times \sqrt[n]{y} = \sqrt[n]{xy}$

Examples:

1) Find the square root of $\sqrt{169x^2}$.

   Solution: Find the factor of the expression $169x^2$: $169 = 13 \times 13$ and $x^2 = x \times x$, now use radical rule: $\sqrt[n]{a^n} = a$.

   Then: $\sqrt{13^2} = 13$ and $\sqrt{x^2} = x$.

   Finally:

   $\sqrt{169x^2} = \sqrt{13^2} \times \sqrt{x^2} = 13 \times x = 13x.$

2) Write this radical in exponential form. $\sqrt[5]{x^7}$

   Solution: To write a radical in exponential form, use this rule: $\sqrt[n]{x^a} = x^{\frac{a}{n}}$.

   Then:

   $\sqrt[5]{x^7} = x^{\frac{5}{7}}.$

3) Simplify. $\sqrt{27x^3}$

   Solution: First factor the expression $27x^3$: $27x^3 = 3^3 \times x \times x \times x$, we need to find perfect squares: $27x^3 = 3^2 \times 3 \times x^2 \times x = 3^2 \times x^2 \times 3x$,

   Then:

   $\sqrt{27x^3} = \sqrt{3^2 \times x^2} \times \sqrt{3x}.$

   Now use radical rule: $\sqrt[n]{a^n} = a$.

   Then:

   $\sqrt{3^2 \times x^2} \times \sqrt{(3x)} = 3x \times \sqrt{3x} = 3x\sqrt{3x}.$

Adding and Subtracting Radical Expressions

Adding and subtracting radical expressions is very similar to adding and subtracting like terms in algebraic expressions. Only numbers and expressions that have the same radical part can be added or subtracted. Radicals with different parts cannot be combined.

✓ Remember, it is not possible to combine "unlike" radical terms.

✓ For numbers with the same radical part, you can simply add or subtract the factors outside the radicals.

Examples:

1) Simplify: $4\sqrt{27} - 2\sqrt{12}$.

Solution: First, let's simplify the radicals individually:

$\sqrt{27} = \sqrt{9 \times 3} = \sqrt{9} \times \sqrt{3} = 3\sqrt{3}$.

$\sqrt{12} = \sqrt{4 \times 3} = \sqrt{4} \times \sqrt{3} = 2\sqrt{3}$.

Now, we can combine the like terms:

$4\sqrt{27} - 2\sqrt{12} = 4(3\sqrt{3}) - 2(2\sqrt{3}) = 12\sqrt{3} - 4\sqrt{3} = 8\sqrt{3}$

2) Simplify: $2\sqrt{125} + \sqrt{5}$.

Solution: The two radical parts are not the same. First, we need to simplify the $2\sqrt{125}$. Then:

$2\sqrt{125} = 2\sqrt{25 \times 5} = 2(\sqrt{25})(\sqrt{5}) = 10\sqrt{5}$.

Now, combine like terms:

$10\sqrt{5} + \sqrt{5} = (10 + 1)\sqrt{5} = 11\sqrt{5}$.

3) Simplify: $6\sqrt{3} + 5\sqrt{3}$.

Solution: Since we have the same radical part($\sqrt{3}$), we can add these two radicals $6\sqrt{3} + 5\sqrt{3} = (6 + 5)\sqrt{3} =$ Therefore, the simplified expression is

Therefore, the simplified expression is $11\sqrt{3}$

Multiplying Radical Expressions

To multiply radical expressions, follow these steps:

- Multiply the numbers and expressions inside the radicals. $\sqrt{a} \times \sqrt{b} = \sqrt{ab}$

- Multiply the numbers and expressions outside of the radicals. $m\sqrt{a} \times n\sqrt{b} = mn\sqrt{ab}$

- Simplify the resulting expression if necessary.

Multiplying Compound Radicals:

For expressions like $(\sqrt{a} + \sqrt{b})(\sqrt{c} + \sqrt{d})$, apply the distributive property (FOIL):

First: $\sqrt{a} \times \sqrt{c} = \sqrt{a \times c}$

Outer: $\sqrt{a} \times \sqrt{d} = \sqrt{a \times d}$

Inner: $\sqrt{b} \times \sqrt{c} = \sqrt{b \times c}$

Last: $\sqrt{b} \times \sqrt{d} = \sqrt{b \times d}$

Examples:

1) Evaluate. $2\sqrt{7} \times \sqrt{3}$

   Multiply the numbers outside of the radicals and the radical parts. Then:

   $2\sqrt{7} \times \sqrt{3} = (2 \times 1) \times (\sqrt{7} \times \sqrt{3}) = 2\sqrt{14}$.

2) Simplify. $4\sqrt{7} \times 2\sqrt{3}$

   Multiply the numbers outside of the radicals and the radical parts. Then, simplify:

   $4\sqrt{7} \times 2\sqrt{3} = (4x \times 2) \times (\sqrt{7} \times \sqrt{3}) = (8)(\sqrt{21})$.

3) Evaluate. $5a\sqrt{7b} \times 2\sqrt{2b}$

   Solution: Multiply the numbers outside of the radicals and the radical parts. Then:

   $5a\sqrt{7b} \times 2\sqrt{2b} = 5a \times 2 \times \sqrt{7b} \times \sqrt{2b} = 10a\sqrt{14b^2}$.

   Simplify: $10a\sqrt{14b^2} = 10a \times \sqrt{14} \times \sqrt{b^2} = 10ab\sqrt{14}$.

4) Multiply the expression. $(\sqrt{2} + \sqrt{3})(\sqrt{2} - \sqrt{3})$

   First: Multiply the first terms in each binomial: $\sqrt{2} \times \sqrt{2} = 2$

   Outer: Multiply the outer terms: $\sqrt{2} \times (-\sqrt{3}) = -\sqrt{6}$

   Inner: Multiply the inner terms: $\sqrt{3} \times \sqrt{2} = \sqrt{6}$

   Last: Multiply the last terms in each binomial: $\sqrt{3} \times (-\sqrt{3}) = -3$

   Now, combine the results: $2 - \sqrt{6} + \sqrt{6} - 3 = -1$

Rationalizing Radical Expressions

Rationalizing radical expressions involves eliminating radicals from the denominator of a fraction. Radical expressions cannot be in the denominator.

- ☑ To get rid of the radical in the denominator, multiply both numerator and denominator by the radical in the denominator.

- ☑ If there is a radical expression combined with another integer in the denominator, multiply both the numerator and denominator by the conjugate of the denominator.

- ☑ The conjugate of $(a + b)$ is $(a - b)$ and vice versa.

- ☑ For cube roots, fourth roots, and so on, the method becomes more involved. You'll need to multiply by a term that allows the radical to become a whole number.

Examples:

1) Simplify: $\frac{12}{\sqrt{5}}$.

   Solution: To simplify the expression, we'll multiply both the numerator and denominator by $\sqrt{5}$. Then:

   $\frac{12}{\sqrt{5}} \times \frac{\sqrt{5}}{\sqrt{5}} = \frac{12\sqrt{5}}{\sqrt{25}} = \frac{12\sqrt{5}}{5}$.

   Now, simplify: $\frac{12\sqrt{5}}{5} = \frac{12}{5} \times \sqrt{5}$.

   Therefore, the simplified form of $\frac{12}{\sqrt{5}}$ is $\frac{12\sqrt{5}}{5}$.

2) Simplify $\frac{8}{\sqrt{10}-3}$.

   Solution: Multiply by the conjugate: $\frac{\sqrt{10}+3}{\sqrt{10}+3} \rightarrow \frac{8}{\sqrt{10}-3} \times \frac{\sqrt{10}+3}{\sqrt{10}+3}$.

   $(\sqrt{10} - 3)(\sqrt{10} + 3) = -9$, then: $\frac{8}{\sqrt{10}-3} \times \frac{\sqrt{10}+3}{\sqrt{10}+3} = \frac{8(\sqrt{10}+3)}{-9}$.

   Use the fraction rule: $\frac{a}{-b} = -\frac{a}{b} \rightarrow \frac{8(\sqrt{10}+3)}{-9} = -\frac{8(\sqrt{10}+3)}{9} = -\frac{8}{9}(\sqrt{10} + 3)$.

   Therefore, the simplified form of $-8(\sqrt{10} + 3)$ is $-\frac{8}{9}(\sqrt{10} + 3)$.

3) Rationalize the expression $\frac{10}{\sqrt[3]{5}}$.

   To remove the cube root, we need two more factors of 5, so:

   $\frac{10}{\sqrt[3]{5}} = \frac{10 \times \sqrt[3]{25}}{\sqrt[3]{5} \times \sqrt[3]{25}} = \frac{10 \times \sqrt[3]{25}}{\sqrt[3]{125}} = \frac{10 \times \sqrt[3]{25}}{5} = 2\sqrt[3]{25}$

Radical Equations

Radical equations are equations in which the variable appears under a radical sign. To solve an equation involving radicals, follow these steps:

    a) Isolate the radical term on one side of the equation.

    b) Square both sides of the equation to remove the radical.

    c) Solve the resulting equation for the variable.

    d) Substitute the obtained solutions into the original equation to verify if they are valid and not extraneous values.

Examples:

1) Solve $\sqrt{x} - 3 = 10$.

    Solution: Add 3 to both sides:

$$\left(\sqrt{x} - 3\right) + 3 = 10 + 3 \rightarrow \sqrt{x} = 13,$$

    square both sides:

$$\left(\sqrt{x}\right)^2 = 13^2 \rightarrow x = 169.$$

    Plugin the value of 169 for x in the original equation and check the answer:

$$x = 169 \rightarrow \sqrt{x} - 3 = \sqrt{169} - 3 = 13 - 3 = 10,$$

    so, the value of 169 for x is correct.

2) What is the value of x in this equation? $4\sqrt{x + 1} = 16$

    Solution: Divide both sides by 4. Then:

$$4\sqrt{x + 1} = 16 \rightarrow \frac{4\sqrt{x+1}}{4} = \frac{16}{4} \rightarrow \sqrt{x + 1} = 4.$$

    Square both sides: $\left(\sqrt{(x + 1)}\right)^2 = 4^2.$

    Then $x + 1 = 16 \rightarrow x = 15.$

    Substitute x by 3 in the original equation and check the answer:

$$x = 15 \rightarrow 4\sqrt{x + 1} = 4\sqrt{15 + 1} = 4\sqrt{16} = 4(4) = 16.$$

    So, the value of 15 for x is correct.

Domain and Range of Radical Functions

To find the domain of the function follow these steps:

a) find all possible values of the variable inside radical.

b) Keep in mind that having a negative number under the square root symbol is not possible. (For cubic roots, we can have negative numbers.)

For ($f(x) = \sqrt[n]{g(x)}$)

- If (n) is even, then ($g(x) \geq 0$).

- If (n) is odd, ($g(x)$) can be any real number.

To find the range of the function: plugin the minimum and maximum values of the variable inside radical into the function.

The range of a radical function of the form $c\sqrt{ax+b} + k$ is: $f(x) \geq k$

Examples:

1) Find the domain and range of the radical function. $y = \sqrt{x+4}$

   Solution: For domain: find non-negative values for radicals: $x + 4 \geq 0$.

   Domain of functions: $\sqrt{f(x)} \rightarrow f(x) \geq 0$, then solve $x + 4 \geq 0 \rightarrow x \geq -4$.

   Domain of the function $y = \sqrt{x+4}$: $x \geq -4$.

   For range: the range of a radical function of the form $c\sqrt{ax+b} + k$ is: $f(x) \geq k$

   For the function $y = \sqrt{x+4}$, the value of k is 0. Then: $f(x) \geq 0$.

   Range of the function $y = \sqrt{x+4}$: $f(x) \geq 0$.

   To summarize: Domain: $x \geq -4$ Range: $f(x) \geq 0$

2) Find the domain and range of the radical function. $y = 7\sqrt{3x+12} + 6$

   Solution: For domain: find non-negative values for radicals: $3x + 12 \geq 0$.

   Domain of functions: $3x + 12 \geq 0 \rightarrow 3x \geq -12 \rightarrow x \geq -4$.

   Domain of the function $y = 7\sqrt{3x+12} + 6$: $x \geq -4$.

   For range: the range of a radical function of the form $c\sqrt{ax+b} + k$ is: $f(x) \geq k$.

   For the function $y = 7\sqrt{3x+12} + 6$, the value of k is 6. Then: $f(x) \geq 6$.

   Range of the function $y = 7\sqrt{3x+12} + 6$: $f(x) \geq 6$. Therefore, the domain of the function is $x \geq -4$, and the range of the function is $f(x) \geq 6$.

Simplify Radicals with Fractions

To simplify radicals with fractions, follow these steps:

- Rewrite the numerator and denominator of the fraction as the product of the prime factorizations.
- Apply the multiplication and division properties of radical expressions to separate the radicals.
- Group the factors that form a perfect square, perfect cube etc.
- Simplify the expression by evaluating the square roots of the perfect squares, cube roots of perfect cubes, etc.

Examples:

1) Simplify. $\sqrt{\frac{4}{49}}$

   Solution: To simplify the radical fraction, rewrite the numerator and denominator as the product of the prime factorizations. So, $\sqrt{\frac{4}{49}} = \sqrt{\frac{2 \times 2}{7 \times 7}}$.

   Since the index of the given radical is 2. You can take one term out of radical for every two same terms multiplied inside the radical sign (perfect square). Then: $\sqrt{\frac{2 \times 2}{7 \times 7}} = \frac{2}{7}$.

2) Simplify the following radical fraction: $\sqrt{\frac{99}{81}}$.

   Solution: Rewrite the numerator and denominator of the fraction as follow: $\sqrt{\frac{99}{81}} =$

   $\sqrt{\frac{3 \times 3 \times 11}{3 \times 3 \times 3 \times 3}}$. Consider the index of the given radical, take out one term of radical for every term that is repeated in an even number inside the radical sign. So, $\sqrt{\frac{3 \times 3 \times 11}{3 \times 3 \times 3 \times 3}} = \frac{3\sqrt{11}}{9}$.

   Simplify, $\frac{3\sqrt{11}}{9} = \frac{\sqrt{11}}{3}$.

6) Write the expression in the simplest radical form. $\sqrt{\frac{242}{63}}$

   Solution: Rewrite this radical fraction as the product of the prime factorizations: $\sqrt{\frac{242}{63}} =$

   $\sqrt{\frac{3 \times 11 \times 11}{3 \times 3 \times 7}}$. Now, take out the terms that are perfect squares, so, $\sqrt{\frac{3 \times 11 \times 11}{3 \times 3 \times 7}} = \frac{11}{3}\sqrt{\frac{3}{7}}$.

Finding Distance of Two Points

To find the distance between two points in a plane, we use the distance formula, which is derived from the Pythagorean theorem.

Given two points with the coordinates $A(x_1, y_1)$ and $B(x_2, y_2)$ in a plane, the distance d between these points is given by:

$$d = \sqrt{(x_2 - x_1)^2 + (y_2 - y_1)^2}$$

Examples:

1) Find the distance between $(3,7)$ and $(-2,-4)$ on the coordinate plane.

   Solution: Use distance of two points formula:

   $d = \sqrt{(x_2 - x_1)^2 + (y_2 - y_1)^2}$.

   Considering that: $(x_1, y_1) = (3,7)$ and $(x_2, y_2) = (-2,-4)$.

   Then:

   $d = \sqrt{(-2 - 3)^2 + (-4 - 7)^2} = \sqrt{(-5)^2 + (-11)^2} = \sqrt{25 + 121} = \sqrt{146}$.

2) Find the distance of two points $(3,6)$ and $(1,-2)$.

   Solution: Use distance of two points formula:

   $d = \sqrt{(x_2 - x_1)^2 + (y_2 - y_1)^2}$.

   Since $(x_1, y_1) = (3,6)$, and $(x_2, y_2) = (1,-2)$.

   Then:

   $d = \sqrt{(1 - 3)^2 + (-2 - 6)^2} = \sqrt{(2)^2 + (-8)^2} = \sqrt{4 + 64} = \sqrt{68} = 8.25$.

   Then: $d = 8.25$.

3) Find the distance between $(4,0)$ and $(8,5)$.

   Solution: Use distance of two points formula:

   $d = \sqrt{(x_2 - x_1)^2 + (y_2 - y_1)^2}$.

   According to: $(x_1, y_1) = (4,0)$ and $(x_2, y_2) = (8,5)$.

   Then: $d = \sqrt{(8 - 4)^2 + (5 - 0)^2} = \sqrt{(4)^2 + (5)^2} = \sqrt{16 + 25} = \sqrt{41} = 6.4$.

   Then: $d = 6.4$.

Chapter 11: Numbers Sequences

 Mathematical concepts covered:

- ◉ Evaluate Recursive Sequences
- ◉ Evaluate Variable Expressions for Number Sequences
- ◉ Write Variable Expressions for Arithmetic Sequences
- ◉ Write Variable Expressions for Geometric Sequences
- ◉ Write a Formula for a Recursive Sequence

Evaluate Recursive Sequences

Let $T_1, T_2, \cdots, T_n, \cdots$ is a sequence where T_n represents the general term of the sequence.

The sequence whose general term defines each term is defined using one or more previous terms. The general formula for a recursive sequence is given by:

$$T_{n+1} = f(T_n)$$

To find the terms of a recursive sequence, according to the recursive formula, a number of previous terms of the sequence are required.

Examples:

1) Find a_2 and a_3, where the first term is $a_1 = -2$, and the general term is $a_n = 2a_{n-1} - 2$.

   Solution: Use the recursive sequence $a_n = 2a_{n-1} - 2$. To find a_2, plug $n = 2$ in $a_n = 2a_{n-1} - 2$. So, $a_2 = 2a_{2-1} - 2 \rightarrow a_2 = 2a_1 - 2$. Now, substitute $a_1 = -2$ into the obtained formula $a_2 = 2a_1 - 2$. Therefore, $a_2 = 2(-2) - 2 = -6$. In the same way, plug in $n = 3$. Then, $a_3 = 2a_{3-1} - 2 \rightarrow a_3 = 2a_2 - 2$. To find the value of a_3, put the obtained value for a_2 in this relation $a_3 = 2a_2 - 2$. Therefore, $a_2 = -3 \rightarrow a_3 = 2(-6) - 2 = -14$.

   The terms are $a_2 = -6$ and $a_3 = -14$.

2) Write the first five terms of the sequence $T_n = T_{n-1} + T_{n-2}$, where $n \geq 2$, $T_1 = 1$ and $T_2 = 2$.

   Solution: Recall that the recursive formula defines each term of a sequence using a previous term or terms, then by looking at the recursive formula $T_n = T_{n-1} + T_{n-2}$ you notice that to generate the terms of the sequence, you need the previous two terms of the sequence. Here you are given the first two terms $T_1 = 1$ and $T_2 = 2$ together with the recursive formula $T_n = T_{n-1} + T_{n-2}$.

   To find the third term which is T_3, plug in $n = 3$. So, $T_3 = T_{3-1} + T_{3-2} \rightarrow T_3 = T_2 + T_1$. Now, substitute the previous terms into the obtained expression. That is $T_3 = 2 + 1 = 3$.

   Similarly, by substituting $n = 4$ and $n = 5$ into the given recursive formula, you get:

   $T_4 = T_{4-1} + T_{4-2} \rightarrow T_4 = T_3 + T_2 \rightarrow T_4 = 3 + 2 = 5$,

   $T_5 = T_{5-1} + T_{5-2} \rightarrow T_5 = T_4 + T_3 \rightarrow T_5 = 5 + 3 = 8$.

   The first five terms of the sequence are 1, 2, 3, 5, and 8.

Evaluate Variable Expressions for Number Sequences

A sequence is an ordered list of numbers where each number is referred to as a term.

Let $x_1, x_2, \cdots, x_i, \cdots$ represent a sequence, with x_i being the general term of the sequence. The first term is denoted as x_1 the second term as x_2, and so on. The ellipses (...) indicate that the pattern continues indefinitely. The subscript i in x_i is known as the index, which helps identify the position of each term in the sequence.

To identify the terms of a sequence, the general term is utilized. By substituting the index value into the general term, the corresponding values for the sequence can be determined. This allows for the generation of other terms within the sequence based on the relationship established by the general term.

Examples:

1) Find the first three terms of the sequence with the general term $a_n = (-1)^{n-2}n$, where n represents the position of a term in the sequence and $n \geq 2$

   Solution: Since $n \geq 2$, the sequence starts at one. So, to find the first term, plug-in n = 2. Then: $a_1 = (-1)^{2-2} \times 2 = 2$. In a similar way, enter the natural numbers in order to find the other terms of the sequence. Therefore,

   Plug in $n = 3$ as $a_2 = (-1)^{3-2} \times 3 = -3$.

   Plug in $n = 4$ as $a_3 = (-1)^{4-1} \times 4 = 4$.

   The first three terms of the sequence are $2, -3$, and 4.

2) Find the first five terms of the sequence with the general term $x_k = \left(-\frac{1}{3}\right)^k$, where k represents the position of a term in the sequence and starts with $k = 1$.

   Solution: To find the first term, plug-in $k = 1$. Then: $x_1 = \left(-\frac{1}{3}\right)^1 = -\frac{1}{3}$. In the same way, to find the 2nd term, plug-in $k = 2$. So, $x_2 = \left(-\frac{1}{3}\right)^2 = \frac{1}{9}$. To find the 3rd term, plug-in $k = 3 \rightarrow x_3 = \left(-\frac{1}{3}\right)^3 = -\frac{1}{27}$. Finally, $k = 4 \rightarrow x_4 = \left(-\frac{1}{3}\right)^4 = \frac{1}{81}$, and $k = 5 \rightarrow$

   $x_5 = \left(-\frac{1}{3}\right)^5 = -\frac{1}{243}$.

   The first three terms of the sequence are $-\frac{1}{3}, \frac{1}{9}, -\frac{1}{27}, \frac{1}{81}$, and $-\frac{1}{243}$.

Write Variable Expressions for Arithmetic Sequences

The given recursive sequence $x_1, x_2, x_3, \cdots$ such that the difference of the terms of the sequence is equal to the same value, is called an arithmetic sequence.

To write the variable expression for the arithmetic sequences, follow these steps:

- Specify the initial values as $x_1 = a$, where 'a' represents the first term of the sequence.
- Determine $d =$ the common difference between terms.
- Express the nth term of the sequence using the formula:

  $x_n = x_1 + (n-1)d$; where $'n'$ represents the position of the term in the sequence.

Examples:

1) Write the variable expression for the following sequence 2, 4, 6, 8, 10, $\cdots$.

    Solution: The given sequence 2, 4, 6, 8, 10, $\cdots$ is an arithmetic sequence with a common difference of 2.

    To write the variable expression for this arithmetic sequence, we can use the formula:

    $x_n = x_1 + (n-1)d$

    where x_n represents the nth term of the sequence, x_1 is the first term, n is the position of the term in the sequence, and d is the common difference.

    For this specific sequence, we have $x_1 = 2$ and $d = 2$.

    Substituting these values into the formula, we get: $x_n = 2 + (n-1) \times 2$,

    Simplifying further, we have: $x_n = 2 + 2n - 2$, then $x_n = 2n$.

    Therefore, the variable expression for the given sequence is $x_n = 2n$.

2) Suppose you have an arithmetic sequence that starts with a first term of 3 and has a common difference of 5.

    Given: $a = 3; d = 5$

    The formula for the nth term of this sequence is:

    $x_n = x_1 + (n-1)d \rightarrow x_n = 3 + (n-1)5 \rightarrow x_n = 3 + 5n - 5 \rightarrow x_n = 5n - 2$

    So, the nth term of the sequence is $5n - 2$.

    Using the formula, you can determine any term in the sequence. For instance:

    For the 1st term $(n = 1)$: $a_1 = 5(1) - 2 = 3$

    For the 2nd term $(n = 2)$: $a_2 = 5(2) - 2 = 8$

    For the 3rd term $(n = 3)$: $a_3 = 5(3) - 2 = 13$

Write Variable Expressions for Geometric Sequences

A geometric sequence is a recursive sequence, denoted as $x_1, x_2, x_3, \cdots$ in which the ratio between consecutive terms remains constant.

To express a geometric sequence using variable notation, follow these steps:

- Specify the initial values as $x_1 = a$.
- Determine the common ratio, denoted by $'r'$, which is the constant ratio between any two consecutive terms.
- Multiply the first term by the product of the number of terms in the common ratio.

Examples:

1) Write an equation to describe for following sequence $3, 9, 27, 81, 243, \cdots$.

   Solution: Let $x_1, x_2, x_3, \cdots$ equivalent to the sequence of the content question. So, the first term is $x_1 = 3$. Now, look for the common ratio between the consecutive terms. So, the common ratio is $r = 2$. Therefore, the sequence is geometric and it can be rewritten as follow:

   $3, 3^2, 3^3, 3^4, 3^5, \cdots$

   You know that the first term of the sequence is multiple of 3, so, the variable expression of this sequence is $a_n = 3^n$. Since the first term is $a_1 = 3$, so, the obtained equation is defined for $n \geq 1$.

2) Write the general formula for the following sequence $4, 8, 32, 64, 128, \cdots$ in terms of variable i.

   Solution: By dividing the consecutive terms by previous terms, you notice that the common ratio is $r = 2$. According to the terms of the sequence, you can see that all terms have the common multiple of 2. Divide all terms of the sequence by 2. So, the following sequence is obtained:

   $2, 4, 8, 16, 32, \cdots$

   It seems that the general formula of the last sequence in terms of variable i is $x_i = (2)^i$, where $i \geq 1$. Therefore, by multiplying this equation by 2, we have:

   $x_i = 2(2)^i$, where $i \geq 1$.

Write a Formula for a Recursive Sequence

To determine the general formula for a given recursive sequence, you can follow these steps:

- Specify the initial values: as a_1 or even a_2.
- Look for a relationship in the previous terms: Examine the relationship among the preceding terms, such as aa_{n-1} or even a_{n-2}
- that holds throughout the sequence. Start by evaluating the differences and ratios of consecutive terms.
- Express the relationship as a function: Once you have identified the relationship, express it as a function of the previous term(s) in the sequence.

Examples:

1) Find the recursive formula corresponding to the following sequence.

$$1, 3, 5, 7, 9, \ldots$$

Solution: Let the first term of this sequence $a_1 = 1$. To find the recursive formula, start by looking at the differences and ratios of consecutive terms. By evaluating the difference of terms with the previous term, you notice that the differences between consecutive terms are all the same. That is, $a_n - a_{n-1} = 2$. In this step, rewrite the obtained rule in terms of a_{n-1}. So, $a_n = a_{n-1} + 2$. Since the first term in the sequence is a_1, the term a_{n-1} is not defined for $n \leq 1$.

2) Find the recursive formula for the following sequence.

$$1, 2, 4, 8, 16, \ldots$$

Solution: Here, let the first term of this sequence $a_1 = 1$. Looking at the terms in this sequence, you can see that each term has an equal ratio to the previous term. Thus, the following relationship is obtained: $\frac{a_n}{a_{n-1}} = 2$. Now, rewrite this rule in terms of a_{n-1}. Therefore, $a_n = 2a_{n-1}$. You know that $a_1 = 1$. It means that the terms a_{n-1} define for $n \geq 2$.

Chapter 12 :
Statistics and Probabilities

 Mathematical concepts covered:

- Mean, Median, Mode, and Range
- Pie Graph
- Scatter Plots
- Probability Problems
- Permutations and Combinations
- Calculate and Interpret Correlation Coefficients
- Regression Line
- Correlation and Causation
- Constant of Variation
- Model Inverse Variation
- Write and Solve Direct Variation Equations

Mean, Median, Mode, and Range

These four measures provide a quick summary of the central tendency and spread of data, helping us understand the distribution and characteristics of the data set.

A. Mean: It's the average of a set of numbers. You calculate it by adding up all the numbers in a data set and then dividing it by the number of data points. Mean: $\frac{sum\ of\ the\ data}{total\ number\ of\ data\ entires}$

B. Median: It's the middle number in a sorted set of data. If there's an even number of data points, the median is the average of the two middle numbers.

C. Mode: It's the number(s) that appear most frequently in a data set. A data set can have one mode, more than one mode, or no mode at all.

D. Range: It's the difference between the largest and smallest values in a data set.

Examples:

1) What is the mode of these numbers? 4, 9, 1, 9, 6, 7

   Solution: Mode: the value in the list that appears most often.

   Therefore, the mode is number 5. There are three number 5 in the data.

2) What is the median of these numbers? 6, 11, 5, 3, 6,

   Solution: Write the numbers in order: 6, 7, 10, 11, 15, 17, 20

   The median is the number in the middle. Therefore, the median is 11.

3) What is the mean of these numbers? 12, 4, 8, 9, 3, 12, 15

   Solution: Use this formula:

   Mean: $\frac{sum\ of\ the\ data}{total\ number\ of\ data\ entires}$.

   Therefore:

   Mean: $= \frac{7+2+3+2+4+8+7+5}{8} = \frac{38}{8} = 4.75$

4) What is the range in this list? 3, 7, 12, 6, 15, 20, 8

   Solution: Range is the difference between the largest value and smallest value in the list.

   The largest value is 20 and the smallest value is 3. Then: $20 - 3 = 17$.

Pie Graph

A Pie Graph, also known as a Pie Chart, is a circular chart that is divided into sectors. Each sector represents the relative size or proportion of a specific value or category within a larger group or dataset. Pie charts represent a snapshot of how a group is broken down into smaller pieces.

Pie charts are ideal when:

- You have a category of data.

- You want to show the proportion of each category to the whole.

- You have a small number of categories.

Examples:

The circle graph below shows all Bob's expenses for last month. Bob spent $790 on his Rent last month.

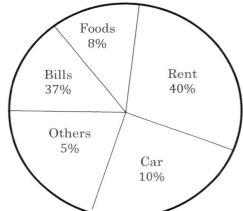

1) How much were Bob's total expenses last month?

    Solution: Total Rent = 790.

    Percent of rent last month= 40%.

    Total expenses:

    $40\% \times x = 790 \rightarrow x = \frac{790}{0.40} = \$1,975.$

    Therefore, Bob's total expenses last month were $1975.

2) How much did Bob spend for foods last month?

    Solution: Total expenses last month = $1,975.

    Percent of food last month = 0.08%.

    Then: $0.08 \times \$1,975 = \$158.$

    Therefore, Bob spent $158 on food last month.

3) How much did Bob spend on his bills last month?

    Solution: Total expenses last month = $1,975.

    Percent of bills last month= 37%.

    Then: $0.37 \times \$1,975 = \$730.75.$ Therefore, Bob spent $730.75 on bills last month

Scatter Plots

A scatter plot is a diagram with points to represent the relationship between two variables.

- On a scatter plot, you can use a trend line to make predictions.
- A scatter plot shows a positive trend when there is a general tendency for the values of the $y-$ variable to increase as the values of the $x-$ variable increase.
- A scatter plot shows a negative trend when the values of the $y-$ variable tend to decrease as the values of the $x-$ variable increase.
- An outlier is an extreme point in a data set that is separated from all other points.

Example:

The following table shows the number of people in a family and the amount of money they spend on movie tickets.

Number of people	1	2	3	4	5	6	7
Money	13	14	17	15	28	18	16

a) Make a scatter plot to represent the data.

b) Does this scatter plot show a positive trend, a negative trend, or no trend?

c) Find the outlier on the scatter plot.

Solution:

Write the ordered pairs. Number of people goes on the $x-$axis, so put the number of people first. Amount of money goes on the $y-$axis, so put the amount of money second. (1,13), (2,14), (3,17), (4,15), (5,28), (6,18), (7,16). Now, graph the ordered pairs. y tends to increase as x increases. So, this scatter plot shows a positive trend.

(5,28) is the outlier because this point is separated from all other points in the data set.

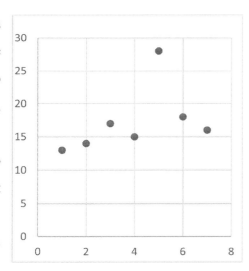

Probability Problems

Probability refers to the measure of the likelihood of an event occurring in the future.

- It is expressed as a number between zero (Can never happen) to 1 (Will always happen).

- Probability can be expressed in different forms, such as fractions, decimals, or a percentage.

- Probability formula: $Probability = \frac{number\ of\ desired\ outcomes}{number\ of\ total\ outcomes}$.

Examples:

1) The bag contains 6 red marbles, 4 blue marbles, and 5 green marbles. If a marble is randomly chosen from the bag, what is the probability of selecting a blue marble?

   Solution: The number of desired outcomes is the number of blue marbles, which is 4. The total number of outcomes is the sum of all the marbles in the bag, which is $6 + 4 + 5 = 15$ Use this formula:

   $Probability = \frac{number\ of\ desired\ outcomes}{number\ of\ total\ outcomes}$.

   Probability of selecting a blue marble $= \frac{4}{6 + 4 + 5} = \frac{4}{15}$.

2) A bag contains 25 balls: five green, six black, eight blue, four brown, a red and one white. If 24 balls are removed from the bag at random, what is the probability that a red ball has been removed?

   Solution: If 24 balls are removed from the bag at random, there will be one ball in the bag. The probability of choosing a red ball is 1 out of 25. Therefore, the probability of not choosing a red ball is 24 out of 25 and the probability of having not a red ball after removing 24 balls is the same.

   The answer is: $\frac{24}{25}$.

Permutations and Combinations

Factorial is the product of all positive integers up to a given number, indicated by an exclamation mark(!).

For a non-negative integer n, the factorial of $n!$, denoted as $n!$, is defined as:

$$n! = n \times (n-1) \times (n-2) \times \cdots \times 3 \times 2 \times 1$$

$$4! = 4 \times 3 \times 2 \times 1.$$

- It is important to note that 0! is defined to be equal to 1: $0! = 1$

❖ Permutations: the number of ways to choose a sample of k elements from a set of n distinct objects, where the order of selection matters and replacements are not allowed and use this formula:

$$nPk = \frac{n!}{(n-k)!}$$

❖ Combination: represent the number of ways to choose a sample of r elements from a set of n distinct objects, where the order of selection does not matter, and replacements are not allowed. The formula is:

$$nCr = \frac{n!}{r!(n-r)!}$$

Examples:

1) How many ways can the first and second place be awarded to 9 people?

   Solution: Since the order matters, (The first and second place are different!) we need to use permutation formula where n is 9 and k is 2.

   Then: $\frac{n!}{(n-k)!} = \frac{9!}{(9-2)!} = \frac{9!}{7!} = \frac{9 \times 8 \times 7!}{7!}$,

   remove 5! from both sides of the fraction.

   Then: $\frac{9 \times 8 \times 7!}{7!} = 9 \times 8 = 72.$

2) How many ways can we pick a team of 3 people from a group of 7?

   Solution: Since the order doesn't matter, we need to use a combination formula where n is 7 and r is 3.

   Then: $\frac{n!}{r!(n-r)!} = \frac{7}{3!(7-3)!} = \frac{7!}{3!(4)!} = \frac{7 \times 6 \times 5 \times 4!}{3!(4)!} = \frac{7 \times 6 \times 5}{3 \times 2 \times 1} = \frac{210}{6} = 35.$

Calculate and Interpret Correlation Coefficients

The correlation coefficient which is represented with sign r determines how close the points of a data set are to being linear. It indicates how closely the data points align with a linear pattern.

The correlation coefficient is used for a set of n data points, (x_1, y_i) where $1 \leq i \leq n$. If the data points form a line with a positive slope, the correlation coefficient is 1. If the data points form a line with a negative slope, the correlation coefficient is -1. A correlation coefficient value closer to 1 or -1 indicates a stronger linear correlation in the data set.

The formula for the correlation coefficient is: $r = \frac{1}{n-1} \cdot \sum_{i=1}^{n} \frac{(x_i - \bar{x})(y_i - \bar{y})}{s_x s_y}$

(where $\bar{x}$ represents the mean of the x−values, $\bar{y}$ represents the mean of the y−values, s_x represents the sample standard deviation of the x−values', s_y represents the sample standard deviation of the y-values, and n represents the number of data points).

If the data points have a positive trend or an increasing trend, the correlation coefficient is positive. If the data points have a negative trend or decreasing trend, the correlation coefficient is negative.

Example:

✎ Sarah is conducting a study on the relationship between the amount of time spent exercising and the number of calories burned. She records the data in the table below. Find the correlation coefficient of this data?

Hours of daily Exercising	The number of Calories Burned
10	75
20	150
30	225
40	300
50	375

Solution: Each row in the above table shows a data point (x_i, y_i). x_i is the number of hours Sarah exercis per day and y_i is the number of calories Sarah burned. You can simply use your calculator to find the above data set's correlation coefficient: $r = 0.968971 \approx 0.969$. The correlation coefficient is positive. So. the data points have a positive trend or increasing trend. The correlation coefficient is so close to 1, So the data set has a strong linear correlation.

Regression Line

The association between scattered data points in any set can be shown with a regression line. In fact, a regression line is a single line that best fits the data and has the least distance from the points. The regression line is used to forecast values based on a data set. The differences between the given values and the values forecasted by the regression line are called residuals. By looking at residuals you can see whether a line fits the data well or not.

The regression line's formula is the same as a line's formula in algebra ($y = mx + b$). In this formula, m is the regression line's slope and b is the y-intercept.

a line where the sum of the residuals' squares is minimized is called the least squares regression line and its formula is as follows: $y = ax + b$, is. the least squares regression line is usually used to make forecasts for a data set.

Remember you should calculate the following values before calculating of a regression line:

✓ The x —values' mean.

✓ The y —values' mean.

✓ The x —values' standard deviation.

✓ The y —values' standard deviation.

✓ The correlation between x and y.

Example:

✎ Find the equation for the least squares' regression line of the following data set. Round your answers to the nearest hundredth. Then interpret the regression line.

x_i	9	15	23	32	45
y_i	24	20	17	13	9

Solution: Use a calculator to find the least squares regression line's equation for the above data set: $y = -0.15875x + 22.53709$. Round your answers to the nearest hundredth: $y = -0.16x + 22.54$. The slope is negative so, there is a negative linear relationship. It means when one variable increases the other variable decreases.

Correlation and Causation

When a variable changes the other variable also changes. Correlation is a statistical measure that explains the relationship between variables. These variables have covariation and change together. This covariation isn't certain because of a direct or indirect causal connection.

Causation shows you when one variable changes, it causes changes in the other variable. In fact, you can see a cause-and-effect relationship between variables.

A correlation doesn't signify causation, but causation always signifies correlation. There are two common situations where a correlation does not indicate causation:

☑ The third variable problem occurs when a confounding variable affects both variables, making them appear causally linked when they are not.

☑ The directionality problem arises when two variables have a correlation, and there may be a causal relationship between them, but it is challenging to determine which variable is the cause of changes in the other.

Examples:

1) Determine whether the following relationship reflects both correlation and causation?

"There is a negative correlation between the number of hours spent studying and the number of hours spent watching TV."

Solution: This relationship reflects correlation but not causation. The negative correlation between the number of hours spent studying and the number of hours spent watching TV suggests that as the time spent studying increases, the time spent watching TV decreases, and vice versa. However, this correlation does not necessarily imply a causal relationship. Other factors, such as personal motivation, time management skills, or external distractions, may influence both studying and TV watching habits.

Therefore, while there is a correlation between the two variables, it does not indicate a direct causal link.

2) Determine whether the following relationship reflects both correlation and causation? "There is a positive correlation between ice cream sales and the number of sunburn cases."

Solution: This relationship reflects correlation but not causation. The positive correlation between ice cream sales and the number of sunburn cases suggests that as ice cream sales increase, the number of sunburn cases also increases. However, this does not mean that ice cream consumption directly causes sunburn. The common factor driving this correlation is likely the warm weather or summer season, which leads to both increased ice cream sales and increased sun exposure. Therefore, while there is a correlation between the two variables, it does not indicate a direct causal relationship.

Constant of Variation

Constant variation refers to the unchanging ratio in a mathematical relationship between two variables. It can be observed in two types: direct variation and inverse variation. In both cases, the constant of variation, denoted ask, remains the same. If an equation follows either of these formats, finding the constant of variation is straightforward:

$$Inverse\ Variation \rightarrow k = xy$$
$$Direct\ Variation \rightarrow k = \frac{y}{x}$$

- Remember that the constant of variation (k) remains the same for every point in the variation relationship.
- If you have a specific point in the variation relationship, you can find the constant of variation by dividing the y-coordinate by the x-coordinate.
- Note that not all equations have a constant of variation and cannot be written in this way.

Examples:

1) If y varies directly as x, and $x = 35$ when $y = 40$, what is the direct variation equation?

Solution: First, put x and y values in the $Direct\ Variation \rightarrow k = \frac{y}{x}$ to find the constant of variation:$Direct\ Variation \rightarrow k = \frac{y}{x} \rightarrow k = \frac{35}{40} \rightarrow k = \frac{7}{8}$. Now using the constant of variation, write the direct variation equation: $y = \frac{7}{8}x$.

2) If y varies inversely as x, and $x = 6$ when $y = 8$, what is the inverse variation equation?

Solution: First, put x and y values in the $Inverse\ Variation \rightarrow k = xy$ to find the constant of variation: $Inverse\ Variation \rightarrow k = xy \rightarrow k = 6 \times 8 \rightarrow k = 48$. Now using the constant of variation, write the inverse variation equation: $y = \frac{48}{x}$.

3) If y varies directly as x, and $y = 50$ when $x = 35$, then what is y when $x = 7$?

Solution: First, use x and y values to find the constant of variation:$Direct\ Variation \rightarrow k = \frac{y}{x} \rightarrow k = \frac{50}{35} \rightarrow k = \frac{10}{7}$. Now using the constant of variation, write the direct variation equation: $y = \frac{10}{7}x$. Find y when $x = 7 \rightarrow y = \frac{10}{7}x \rightarrow y = \frac{10}{7} \times 7 \rightarrow y = \frac{70}{7} = 10$.

Model Inverse Variation

The inverse variation is a kind of variables that is represented in the form of $y = \frac{k}{x}$. In this relationship, x and y are 2 variables and k is a constant value. It shows that when the value of one number increases, the value of the other number changes inversely and decreases. The value of k remains unchanged and it can't be zero ($k \neq 0$).

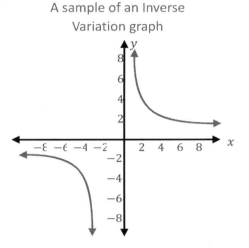

A sample of an Inverse Variation graph

You can make the table of inverse variation by putting the one quantity's values in the equation and table, then find the other quantity.

If you have an inverse variation and want to solve for an unknown, you can follow these steps:

- Determine x, and y (the inputs and the outputs).
- Find the variation's constant. Sometimes you should multiply y by a particular x power to find the variation's constant.
- Write an equation for the relationship by using the constant of variation.
- Find the unknown value by Substitution known values into the equation.

Example:

✎ According to the following table, determine if y values change inversely with x. If yes, write an equation for the inverse variation and show it in a graph.

x	y
3	16
4	12
6	8
8	6

Solution: In a table with inverse changes the product of all x and y pairs of its data is the same value. you can see that the product of any pair of x and y is equal to 48, so $k = 48$. write an equation for the inverse variation:

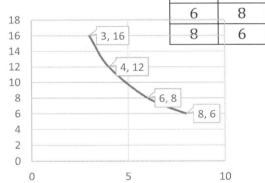

$$y = \frac{k}{x} \rightarrow y = \frac{48}{x}$$

You can make a graph of the equation $y = \frac{48}{x}$ with points from the table as follows:

Write and Solve Direct Variation Equations

Direct variation expresses a math relationship between 2 variables. It shows one variable, y changes directly with other variable x and when x increases, y also increases, and conversely, when x decreases, y decreases. It is important to note that the ratio in direct variation always remains the same.

A two-variables linear equation's slope-intercept form is as follows: $y = mx + b$. If we consider the y −intercept occurs at the point of $(0,0)$ and substitute the slope (m) with the constant of variation (k), we obtain a direct variation equation: $y = kx$. In this equation, k represents the constant of variation, which is a value that remains unchanged throughout the relationship.

In direct variation, the proportion between the variables remains the same, leading to a graph that always forms a straight line.

Examples:

1) If y varies directly with x and $y = 24$ when $x = 8$, find y when $x = 9$.

    Solution: First, you should find the constant of variation. Put $x = 8$nd $y = 24$ into the direct variation equation to find the value of k: $y = kx \rightarrow 21 = k \times 7 \rightarrow k = \frac{24}{8} = 3 \rightarrow k = 3$. Now, use $k = 3$ to find y when $x = 9$: $y = kx \rightarrow y = 3 \times 9 = 27 \rightarrow y = 27$.

2) If y varies directly with x and $y = 25$ when $x = 5$, find x when $y = 35$.

    Solution: First, you should find the constant of variation. Put $x = 5$ and $y = 25$ into the direct variation equation to find the value of k: $y = kx \rightarrow 25 = k \times 5 \rightarrow k = \frac{25}{5} = 5 \rightarrow k = 5$. Now, use $k = 4$ to find x when $y = 35$: $y = kx \rightarrow 35 = 5 \times x = x = \frac{35}{5} = 7 \rightarrow x = 7$.

3) If y varies directly with x and $y = 56$ when $x = 7$, find y when $x = 10$.

    Solution: First, you should find the constant of variation. Put $x = 7$ and $y = 56$ into the direct variation equation to find the value of k: $y = kx \rightarrow 56 = k \times 7 \rightarrow k = \frac{56}{7} = 8 \rightarrow k = 8$. Now, use $k = 10$ to find y when $x = 10$: $y = kx \rightarrow y = 8 \times 10 = 80 \rightarrow y = 80$.

Algebra 1 Practice Tests

Time to Test

Time to refine your skill with a practice examination.

Take a REAL Algebra 1 test to simulate the test day experience. After you've finished, score your test using the answer key.

Before You Start

- You'll need a pencil, calculator, and a timer to take the test.
- It's okay to guess. You won't lose any points if you're wrong.
- After you've finished the test, review the answer key to see where you went wrong.

Graphing calculators are Not permitted for Algebra 1 Tests.

Good Luck!

Algebra 1 Practice Test 1

✓ **30 Questions**

✓ **You may use a calculator for this test.**

Administered *Month Year*

1) If a, b and c are positive integers and $3a = 7b = 2c$, then the value of $3a + 7b + 4c$ is how many times the value of a?

   A. 12

   B. 16

   C. 12.5

   D. 14

2) If $f(x^2) = 5x + 3$, for all positive value of x, what is the value of $f(121)$?

   A. -58

   B. 58

   C. 56

   D. -56

3) If a and b are solutions of the following equation, which of the following is the ratio $\frac{a}{b}$? $(a > b)$

$$2x^2 + 12x + 13 = 4x + 23$$

   A. $\frac{1}{5}$

   B. -5

   C. $-\frac{1}{5}$

   D. 5

4) If $x \neq -7$ and $x \neq 6$, which of the following is equivalent to $\frac{1}{\frac{1}{x-3}+\frac{1}{x+8}}$?

   A. $\frac{(x-3)(x+8)}{(x-3)+(x+8)}$

   B. $\frac{(x+8)+(x-3)}{(x+8)(x-3)}$

   C. $\frac{(x+8)(x-3)}{(x+8)-(x+3)}$

   D. $\frac{(x+8)+(x-3)}{(x+8)-(x-3)}$

5) A line in the xy-plane passes through origin and has a slope of $\frac{1}{3}$. Which of the following points lies on the line?

   A. $(3,6)$

   B. $(6,3)$

   C. $(9, 3)$

   D. $(3,9)$

6) Which of the following is the solution of the following inequality?

$$3x + 6.5 > 11x - 2.5 - 3.5x$$

   A. $x < 2$

   B. $x > 2$

   C. $x \leq 5$

   D. $x \geq 5$

Gender	Under 45	45 or older	total
Male	12	14	26
Female	16	8	24
Total	28	22	50

7) The table above shows the distribution of age and gender for 40 employees in a company. If one employee is selected at random, what is the probability that the employee selected be either a female under age 45 or a male age 45 or older?

A. $\frac{2}{5}$ C. $\frac{3}{25}$

B. $\frac{3}{5}$ D. $\frac{4}{25}$

8) If a parabola with equation $y = ax^2 + 3x + 15$, where a is constant, passes through point $(2, 5)$, what is the value of a^2?

A. -2 C. -16

B. 2 D. 16

9) John works for an electric company. He receives a monthly salary of \$4,100 plus 12% of all his monthly sales as a bonus. If x is the number of all John's sales per month, which of the following represents John's monthly revenue in dollars?

A. $0.12x$ C. $0.12x + 4,100$

B. $0.88x - 4,100$ D. $0.88x + 4,100$

10) What is the value of $f(2)$ for the following function f?

$$f(x) = x^4 - 8x$$

A. 1   C. 4

B. 0   D. 8

11) John buys a pepper plant that is 9 inches tall. With regular watering the plant grows 4 inches a year. Writing John's plant's height as a function of time, what does the y −intercept represent?

    A. The y −intercept represents the rate of grows of the plant which is 9 in.

    B. The y −intercept represents the starting height of 9 in.

    C. The y −intercept represents the rate of growth of plant which is 4 in. per year.

    D. There is no y −intercept.

12) What is the length of AB in the following figure if $AE = 5$, $CD = 3$ and $AC = 16$?

    A. 32

    B. 8

    C. 12

    D. 10

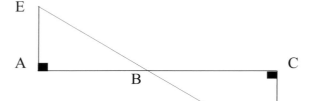

13) If $y = nx + 7$, where n is a constant, and when $x = 6$, $y = 14$, what is the value of y when $x = 6$?

    A. 36   C. 16

    B. 15   D. 13

14) If $8 + 4x$ is 10 more than 14, what is the value of $8x$?

    A. 32   C. 16

    B. 64   D. 128

15) If a gas tank can hold 40 gallons, how many gallons does it contain when it is $\frac{5}{8}$ full?

    A. 40   C. 25

    B. 50   D. 64

16) In the xy-plane, the point $(2,5)$ and $(1,4)$ are online A. Which of the following equations of lines is parallel to line A?

A. $y = 3x$

B. $y = \frac{x}{2}$

C. $y = 2x$

D. $y = x$

17) A football team won exactly 40% of the games it played during the last session. Which of the following could be the total number of games the team played last season?

A. 43

B. 45

C. 48

D. 34

18) The capacity of a red box is 25% bigger than the capacity of a blue box. If the red box can hold 50 equal sized books, how many of the same books can the blue box hold?

A. 15

B. 35

C. 25

D. 40

19) The sum of four different negative integers is -46. If the smallest of these integers is -13, what is the largest possible value of one of the other three integers?

A. -11

B. -8

C. -10

D. -9

20) If x is greater than 2 and less than 3, which of the following is true?

A. $x < \sqrt{x^2 + 2} < \sqrt{x^2} + 2$

B. $x < \sqrt{x^2 + 2} < \sqrt{x^2 + 2}$

C. $\sqrt{x^2 + 2} < x < \sqrt{x^2} + 2$

D. $\sqrt{x^2} + 2 < \sqrt{x^2 + 2} < x$

21) The ratio of boys and girls in a class is 4:5. If there are 72 students in the class, how many more boys should be enrolled to make the ratio 1:1?

A. 40

B. 12

C. 8

D. 32

22) If $f(x) = 2x + 3(x + 4) + 5$ then $f(2x) = ?$

    A. $10x + 17$ C. $12x + 17$

    B. $10x - 17$ D. $12x - 17$

Questions 23, 24 and 25 are based on the following data.

Types of air pollutions in 10 cities of a country

Type of Pollution	Number of Cities									
A	░	░	░	░	░	░	░	░		
B	░	░	░	░	░	░				
C	░	░								
D	░	░	░	░	░	░	░	░	░	
E	░	░	░	░	░	░				
	1	2	3	4	5	6	7	8	9	10

23) If a is the mean (average) of the number of cities in each pollution type category, b is the mode, and c is the median of the number of cities in each pollution type category, then which of the following must be true?

    A. $b < a < c$ C. $a = c$

    B. $c < a < b$ D. $b < c = a$

24) How many cities should be added to type of pollutions C until the ratio of cities in type of pollution C to cities in type of pollution A will be 0.75?

    A. 8   C. 6

    B. 4   D. 2

25) What percent of cities are in the type of pollution B, C, and E respectively?

    A. 60%, 60%, 20%   C. 1.50%, 1.20%, 1.30%

    B. 1.50%, 1.20%, 1.60%   D. 50%, 20%, 60%

26) In the rectangle below if $y > 6$ cm and the area of rectangle is 42 cm^2 and the perimeter of the rectangle is 26 cm, what is the value of x and y respectively?

    A. 7, 5

    B. 6, 13

    C. 6, 7

    D. 7, 13

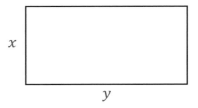

27) In the triangle below, if the measure of angle A is 37 degrees, then what is the value of y? (Figure is NOT drawn to scale)

    A. 55

    B. 50

    C. 75

    D. 70

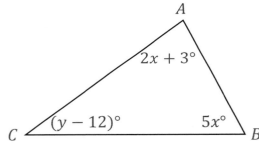

28) The following graph shows the marks of six students in mathematics. What is the mean (average) of the marks?

    A. 13.5

    B. 14

    C. 14.5

    D. 15

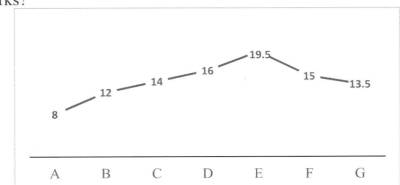

29) Which of the following values for x and y satisfy the following system of equations?

$$\begin{cases} x + 2y = 3 \\ -4x - 3y = -7 \end{cases}$$

A. $x = -1, \ y = 0$

B. $x = 0, \ y = 1$

C. $x = 1, \ y = -1$

D. $x = 1, \ y = 1$

30) Solve the following inequality.

$$\left|\frac{x}{4} - x + 2 + 7\right| < 3$$

A. $-8 < x < 14$ C. $8 < x < 16$

B. $-14 < x < 8$ D. $-16 < x < -8$

STOP

This is the End of this Test. You may check your work on this Test if you still have time.

Algebra 1 Practice Test 2

✓ **30 Questions**

✓ **You may use a calculator for this test.**

Administered *Month Year*

1) If $xp + 4yq = 15$ and $xp + 3yq = 9$, what is the value of yq?

    A. 10   C. 6

    B. 4   D. 8

2) If $x^2 + 4$ and $x^2 - 4$ are two factors of the polynomial $3x^4 + n$ and n is a constant, what is the value of n?

    A. -48 C. 42

    B. -24 D. 32

3) If $5x - 4 = 9.5$, what is the value of $2x + 3$?

    A. 8.4   C. 10.4

    B. 9.4   D. 6.4

4) If the function f is defined by $f(x) = x^2 + 3x - 7$, which of the following is equivalent to $f(4t^2)$?

    A. $16t^4 + 10t^2 - 7$ C. $12t^4 + 7t^2 - 12t$

    B. $16t^4 + 12t^2 - 7$ D. $16t^4 + 12t^2 + 7$

5) The circle graph below shows all Mr. Green's expenses for last month. If he spent $550 on his car, how much did he spend on his rent?

    A. $448   Mr. Green's monthly expenses

    B. $884

    C. $848

    D. $484

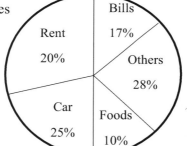

6) The radius of circle A is four times the radius of circle B. If the circumference of circle A is 16π, what is the area of circle B?

    A. 8π C. 4π

    B. 2π D. 16π

0.ABC   0.0D

7) The letters represent two decimals listed above. One of the decimals is equivalent to $\frac{7}{8}$

and the other is equivalent to $\frac{1}{50}$. What is the product of C and D?

A. 2

B. 5

C. 10

D. 15

8) In the diagram below, circle A represents the set of all even numbers, circle B represents the set of all negative numbers, and circle C represents the set of all multiples of 6. Which number could be replaced with y?

A. 0

B. 12

C. -18

D. -21

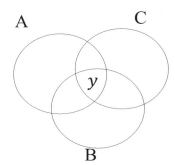

9) There are only red and blue cards in a box. The probability of choosing a red card in the box at random is one-third. If there are 144 blue cards, how many cards are in the box?

A. 162

B. 362

C. 326

D. 216

10) Both $(x = -2)$ and $(x = 1)$ are solutions for which of the following equations?

I. $x^2 - 3x + 5 = 0$

III. $2x^2 + 2x - 4 = 0$

II. $3x^2 - 3x = 6$

A. I only

B. I and III

C. II and III

D. I, II and III

11) In a certain bookshelf of a library, there are 50 biology books, 68 history books, and 82 language books. What is the ratio of the number of biology books to the total number of books on this bookshelf?

   A. $\frac{1}{6}$

   B. $\frac{1}{4}$

   C. $\frac{1}{5}$

   D. $\frac{3}{4}$

12) The following table represents the value of x and function $f(x)$. Which of the following could be the equation of the function $f(x)$?

   A. $f(x) = x^2 + 2$

   B. $f(x) = x^2 - 2$

   C. $f(x) = \sqrt{x + 3}$

   D. $f(x) = \sqrt{x} + 3$

x	$f(x)$
1	4
4	5
9	6
16	7

13) In the figure below, what is the value of x?

   A. 52

   B. 63

   C. 65

   D. 117

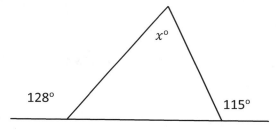

14) If $(4^a)^b = 256$, then what is the value of ab?

   A. 2

   B. 6

   C. 4

   D. 8

15) What is the sum of $\sqrt{x} - 9$ and $\sqrt{x - 9}$ when $\sqrt{x} = 5$?

   A. -4

   B. -1

   C. 0

   D. 4

16) What is the average (arithmetic mean) of all integers from 15 to 21?

A. 18

B. 18.5

C. 17

D. 19.5

17) What is the value of $\frac{7a-1}{6}$, if $-3a + 5a + 7a = 63$?

A. 7.5

B. 7

C. 8

D. 8.5

18) What is the value of $|-16 - 7| - 12 + 3$?

A. -14

B. 14

C. 12

D. -12

19) A container holds 1.6 gallons of water when it is $\frac{8}{35}$ full. How many gallons of water does the container hold when it's full?

A. 8

B. 7

C. 12

D. 15

20) The table represents different values of function $g(x)$. What is the value of $4g(-2) - 2g(4)$?

x	-2	-1	0	2	3	4
$g(x)$	3	2	1	0	-2	-4

A. -20

B. -12

C. 12

D. 20

21) f a is an odd integer divisible by 7. Which of the following must be divisible by 5?

A. $a - 4$

B. $a + 4$

C. $4a$

D. $5a - 5$

22) If $(x - 3)^2 = 9$ which of the following could be the value of $(x - 2)(x - 5)$?

    A. 3   C. -4

    B. 4   D. -3

23) On the following figure, what is the area of the quadrilateral ABCD?

    A. 12

    B. 32

    C. 24

    D. 42

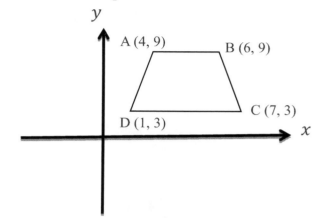

24) What is the x-intercept of the line with equation $5x - 3y = 8$?

    A. 3   C. $\frac{8}{5}$

    B. -5 D. $\frac{3}{5}$

25) The base of the right triangle is 10 feet, and the interior angles are 45-45-90. What is its area?

    A. 50 square feet   C. 40 square feet

    B. 10 square feet   D. 100 square feet

26) In 1999, the average worker's income increased \$3,000 per year starting from \$19,000 annual salary. Which equation represents income greater than average? (I = income, x = number of years after 1999)

    A. $I > 3{,}000\, x + 19{,}000$

    B. $I > -3{,}000\, x + 19{,}000$

    C. $I < -3{,}000\, x + 19{,}000$

    D. $I < 3{,}000\, x - 19{,}000$

27) The Jackson Library is ordering some bookshelves. If x is the number of bookshelves the library wants to order, which each cost $200 and there is a one-time delivery charge of $500, which of the following represents the total cost, in dollar, per bookshelf?

A. $200x + 500$

B. $200 + 500x$

C. $\frac{200x+500}{200}$

D. $\frac{200x+500}{x}$

28) What is the solution to the following inequality?

$$|x - 3| \geq 12$$

A. $x \geq 15 \ \cup \ x \leq -9$

B. $-9 \leq x \leq 15$

C. $x \geq 15$

D. $x \leq -9$

29) If the area of the following rectangular ABCD is 120, and E is the midpoint of AB, what is the area of the shaded part?

A. 30

B. 60

C. 40

D. 80

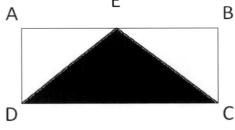

30) Which of the following is equivalent to $5 < -4x - 3 < 13$?

A. $-4 < x < -2$

B. $2 < x < 4$

C. $3 < x < 8$

D. $\frac{-3}{5} < x < \frac{1}{2}$

STOP

This is the End of this Test. You may check your work on this Test if you still have time.

Answers and Explanations

Answer Key

✳ Now, it's time to review your results to see where you went wrong and what areas you need to improve!

Algebra 1 Tests

Practice Test - 1					
1	A	11	B	21	C
2	B	12	D	22	A
3	B	13	D	23	C
4	A	14	A	24	B
5	C	15	C	25	D
6	A	16	D	26	C
7	B	17	B	27	D
8	D	18	D	28	B
9	C	19	C	29	D
10	B	20	A	30	C

Practice Test - 2					
1	C	11	B	21	D
2	A	12	D	22	B
3	A	13	B	23	C
4	B	14	C	24	C
5	D	15	C	25	A
6	C	16	A	26	A
7	C	17	C	27	D
8	C	18	B	28	A
9	D	19	B	29	B
10	C	20	D	30	A

Answers and Explanations

Practice Tests 1

1) Answer: A.

$3a = 7b \rightarrow b = \frac{3a}{7}$ and $\quad 3a = 2c \rightarrow c = \frac{3a}{2}$

$3a + 7b + 4c = 3a + \left(7 \times \frac{3a}{7}\right) + \left(4 \times \frac{3a}{2}\right) = 3a + 3a + 6a = 12a$; The value of

$3a + 7b + 2c$ is 12 times the value of a.

2) Answer: B.

$x^2 = 121 \rightarrow x = 11$ (Positive value) $\quad$ Or $x = -11$ (negative value)

Since x is positive, then:

$f(121) = f(11^2) = 5(11) + 3 = 55 + 3 = 58$

3) Answer: B.

$2x^2 + 12x + 13 = 4x + 23 \rightarrow 2x^2 - 4x + 12x + 13 - 23 = 0 \rightarrow 2x^2 + 8x - 10 = 0$

$\rightarrow 2(x^2 + 4x - 5) = 0 \rightarrow$ Divide both sides by 2. Then:

$x^2 + 4x - 5 = 0$, Find the factors of the quadratic equation.

$\rightarrow (x + 5)(x - 1) = 0 \rightarrow x = -5$ or $x = 1$

$a > b$, then: $a = -5$ and $b = 1 \rightarrow \frac{a}{b} = \frac{-5}{1} = -5$

4) Answer: A.

To rewrite $\frac{1}{\frac{1}{x-3}+\frac{1}{x+8}}$, first simplify $\frac{1}{x-3} + \frac{1}{x+8}$.

$\frac{1}{x-3} + \frac{1}{x+8} = \frac{(x+8)}{(x-3)(x+8)} + \frac{(x-3)}{(x+8)(x-3)} = \frac{(x+8)+(x-3)}{(x+8)(x-3)}$

Then: $\frac{1}{\frac{1}{x-3}+\frac{1}{x+8}} = \frac{1}{\frac{(x+8)+(x-3)}{(x+8)(x-3)}} = \frac{(x+8)(x-3)}{(x+8)+(x-3)}$. (Remember, $\frac{1}{\frac{1}{x}} = x$)

This result is equivalent to the expression in choice A.

5) Answer: C.

First, find the equation of the line. All lines through the origin are of the form $y = mx$,

so the equation is $y = \frac{1}{3}x$. Of the given choices, only choice C (9,3), satisfies this

equation: $y = \frac{1}{3}x \rightarrow 3 = \frac{1}{3}(9) = 3$

6) Answer: A.

$3x + 6.5 > 11x - 2.5 - 3.5x \rightarrow$ Combine like terms:

$3x + 6.5 > 7.5x - 2.5 \rightarrow$ Subtract $3x$ from both sides:

$6.5 > 4.5x - 2.5$; Add 2.5 to both sides of the inequality.

$9 > 4.5x$, Divide both sides by 4.5: $\frac{9}{4.5} > x \rightarrow x < 2$

7) Answer: B.

Of the 40 employees, there are 16 females under age 45 and 14 males age 45 or older.

Therefore, the probability that the person selected will be either a female under age 45 or a male age 45 or older is: $\frac{16}{50} + \frac{14}{50} = \frac{30}{50} = \frac{3}{5}$

8) Answer: D.

Plug in the values of x and y of the point $(2, 5)$ in the equation of the parabola. Then:

$5 = a(2)^2 + 3(2) + 15 \rightarrow 5 = 4a + 6 + 15 \rightarrow 5 = 4a + 21$

$\rightarrow 4a = 5 - 21 = -27 \rightarrow a = \frac{-16}{4} = -4 \rightarrow a^2 = (-4)^2 = 16$

9) Answer: C.

x is the number of all John's sales per month and 12% of it is:

$12\% \times x = 0.12x$

John's monthly revenue: $0.12x + 4,100$

10) Answer: B.

The output value is 0. Then: $x = 2$

$f(x) = x^4 - 8x \rightarrow f(2) = 2^4 - 8(2) = 16 - 16 = 0$

11) Answer: B.

To solve this problem, first recall the equation of a line: $y = mx + b$; Where, $m = slope$ and $y = y - intercept$

Remember that slope is the rate of change that occurs in a function and that the $y-$intercept is the y value corresponding to $x = 0$.

Since the height of John's plant is 9 inches tall when he gets it. Time (or x) is zero.

The plant grows 4 inches per year. Therefore, the rate of change of the plant's height is 4. The $y-$intercept represents the starting height of the plant which is 9 inches.

12) Answer: D.

Two triangles ΔBAE and ΔBCD are similar. Then:

$\frac{AE}{CD} = \frac{AB}{BC} \rightarrow \frac{5}{3} = \frac{x}{16-x} \rightarrow 5(16-x) = 3x \rightarrow 5x + 3x = 5 \times 16 \rightarrow 8x = 80 \rightarrow x = 10$

13) Answer: D.

Substituting 6 for x and 14 for y in $y = nx + 7$ gives $14 = (n)(6) + 7$

which gives $n = 1$. Hence, $y = x + 7$. Therefore, when $x = 6$, the value of y is:

$$y = 6 + 7 = 13$$

14) Answer: A.

The description $8 + 4x$ is 10 more than 14 can be written as the equation $8 + 4x = 10 + 14$, which is equivalent to $8 + 4x = 24$. Subtracting 8 from each side gives:

$4x = 16$.

Since $8x$ is 2 times $4x$, multiplying both sides of $4x = 16$ by 2 gives $8x = 32$

15) Answer: C.

$\frac{5}{8} \times 40 = \frac{200}{8} = 25$

16) Answer: D.

The slop of line A is: $m = \frac{y_2 - y_1}{x_2 - x_1} = \frac{5-4}{2-1} = 1$

Parallel lines have the same slope and only choice D ($y = x$) has slope of 1.

17) Answer: B.

Choices A, C and D are incorrect because 40% of each of the numbers is a non-whole number.

    A. 43, 40% of $43 = 0.40 \times 43 = 17.2$

    B. 45, 40% of $45 = 0.40 \times 45 = 18$

    C. 48, 40% of $48 = 0.40 \times 48 = 19.2$

    D. 34, 40% of $34 = 0.40 \times 34 = 13.6$

Only choice B gives a whole number.

18) Answer: D.

The capacity of a red box is 25% bigger than the capacity of a blue box and it can hold 50 books. Therefore, we want to find a number that 25% bigger than that number is

50. Let x be that number. Then: $1.25 \times x = 50$, Divide both sides of the equation by 1.25. Then: $x = \frac{50}{1.25} = 40$

19) Answer: C.

The smallest number is -13. To find the largest possible value of one of the other three integers, we need to choose the smallest possible integers for three of them. Let x be the largest number. Then: $-46 = (-13) + (-12) + (-11) + x \rightarrow -46 = -36 + x \rightarrow x = -46 + 36 = -10$

20) Answer: A.

Let x be equal to 2.5, then: $x = 2.5$

$\sqrt{x^2 + 2} = \sqrt{2.5^2 + 2} = \sqrt{8.25} \approx 2.87$

$\sqrt{x^2} + 2 = \sqrt{2.5^2} + 2 = 2.5 + 2 = 4.5$

Then, option A is correct: $x < \sqrt{x^2 + 2} < \sqrt{x^2} + 2$

21) Answer: C.

The ratio of boys to girls is 4:5. Therefore, there are 4 boys out of 9 students. To find the answer, first divide the total number of students by 9, then multiply the result by 4.

$72 \div 9 = 8 \Rightarrow 4 \times 8 = 32$

There are 32 boys and 40 (72 – 32) girls. So, 8 more boys should be enrolled to make the ratio 1:1.

22) Answer: A.

If $f(x) = 2x + 3(x + 4) + 5$, then find $f(2x)$ by substituting $2x$ for every x in the function. This gives: $f(2x) = 2(2x) + 3(2x + 4) + 5$,

It simplifies to: $f(2x) = 4x + 6x + 12 + 5 = 10x + 17$

23) Answer: C.

Let's find the mean (average), mode and median of the number of cities for each type of pollution.

Number of cities for each type of pollution: 6, 2, 5, 8, 9

$$average\ (mean) = \frac{sum\ of\ terms}{number\ of\ terms} = \frac{6+2+5+8+9}{5} = \frac{30}{5} = 6$$

Median is the number in the middle. To find median, first list numbers in order from smallest to largest: 2, 5, 6, 8, 9. The median of the data is 6.

Mode is the number which appears most often in a set of numbers. Therefore, there is no mode in the set of numbers. Median = Mean, then, $a=c$

24) Answer: B.

Let the number of cities should be added to type of pollutions C be x. Then: $\frac{x+2}{8} =$

$0.75 \rightarrow x + 2 = 8 \times 0.75 \rightarrow x + 2 = 6 \rightarrow x = 4$

25) Answer: D.

Percent of cities in the type of pollution B: $\frac{5}{10} \times 100 = 50\%$

Percent of cities in the type of pollution C: $\frac{2}{10} \times 100 = 20\%$

Percent of cities in the type of pollution E: $\frac{6}{10} \times 100 = 60\%$

26) Answer: C.

The perimeter of the rectangle is: $2x + 2y = 26 \rightarrow x + y = 13 \rightarrow x = 13 - y$

The area of the rectangle is: $x \times y = 42 \rightarrow (13 - y)(y) = 42 \rightarrow y^2 - 13y + 42 = 0$

Solve the quadratic equation by factoring method. $(y - 6)(y - 7) = 0$

$y = 6$ (Unacceptable, because y must be greater than 6)

or $y = 7 \rightarrow x \times y = 42 \rightarrow x \times 7 = 42 \rightarrow x = 6$

27) Answer: D.

In the figure angle A is labeled $(2x + 3)$ and it measures 37. Thus, $2x + 3 = 37$ and $2x = 34$ or $x = 17$.

That means that angle B, which is labeled $(5x)$, must measure $5 \times 17 = 85$.

Since the three angles of a triangle must add up to 180, $37 + 85 + y - 12 = 180$, then: $y + 110 = 180 \rightarrow y = 180 - 110 = 70$

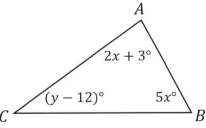

28) Answer: B.

$$average\ (mean) = \frac{sum\ of\ terms}{number\ of\ terms} = \frac{8+12+14+16+19.5+15+13.5}{7} = 14$$

29) Answer: D.

$$\begin{cases} x + 2y = 3 \\ -4x - 3y = -7 \end{cases} \rightarrow \quad \text{Multiply the top equation by 4 then,}$$

$$\begin{cases} 4x + 8y = 12 \\ -4x - 3y = -7 \end{cases} \rightarrow \quad \text{Add two equations,}$$

$5y = 5 \rightarrow y = 1$, plug in the value of y into the first equation:

$x + 2y = 3 \rightarrow x + 2(1) = 3 \rightarrow x + 2 = 3$

Add -2 from both sides of the equation.

Then: $x + 2 - 2 = 3 - 2 \rightarrow x = 1$

30) Answer: C.

$$\left| \frac{x}{4} - x + 2 + 7 \right| < 3 \rightarrow \left| -\frac{3}{4}x + 9 \right| < 3 \rightarrow -3 < -\frac{3}{4}x + 9 < 3$$

Subtract 9 from all sides of inequality.

$$\rightarrow -3 - 9 < -\frac{3}{4}x + 9 - 9 < 3 - 9 \rightarrow -12 < -\frac{3}{4}x < -6$$

Multiply all sides by 4.

$$\rightarrow 4 \times (-12) < 4 \times \left(-\frac{3x}{4} \right) < 4 \times (-6) \rightarrow -48 < -3x < -24$$

Divide all sides by -3. (Remember that when you divide all sides of an inequality by a negative number, the inequality sign will be swapped. $<$ becomes $>$)

$$\rightarrow \frac{-48}{-3} > \frac{-3x}{-3} > \frac{-24}{-3} \rightarrow 16 > x > 8 \rightarrow 8 < x < 16$$

Answers and Explanations

Practice Tests 2

1) Answer: C.

$xp + 4yq = 15 \rightarrow xp = 15 - 4yq$ (1)

$xp + 3yq = 9$ (2)

(1) in (2) $\rightarrow 15 - 4yq + 3yq = 9 \rightarrow 15 - yq = 9 \rightarrow yq = 15 - 9 = 6$

2) Answer: A.

$3x^4 + n = a(x^2 + 4)(x^2 - 4) = ax^4 - 16a \rightarrow a = 3$

And $n = -16a = -16 \times 3 = -48$

3) Answer: A.

$5x - 4 = 9.5 \rightarrow 5x = 9.5 + 4 = 13.5 \rightarrow x = \dfrac{13.5}{5} = 2.7$

Then; $2x + 3 = 2(2.7) + 3 = 5.4 + 3 = 8.4$

4) Answer: B.

$f(x) = x^2 + 3x - 7$

$f(4t^2) = (4t^2)^2 + 3(4t^2) - 7 = 16t^4 + 12t^2 - 7$

5) Answer: D.

Let x be all expenses, then $\dfrac{25}{100}x = \$550 \rightarrow x = \dfrac{100 \times \$550}{25} = \$2,200$

He spent for his rent: $\dfrac{22}{100} \times \$2,200 = \$484$

6) Answer: C.

Let P be circumference of circle A, then; $2\pi r_A = 16\pi \rightarrow r_A = 8$

$r_A = 4r_B \rightarrow r_B = \dfrac{8}{4} = 2 \rightarrow$ Area of circle B is $\pi r_B^2 = 4\pi$

7) Answer: C.

$\dfrac{7}{8} = 0.875 \rightarrow C = 5; \dfrac{1}{20} = 0.02 \rightarrow D = 2 \rightarrow C \times D = 5 \times 2 = 10$

8) Answer: C.

y is the intersection of the three circles. Therefore, it must be even (from circle A), negative (from circle B), and multiple of 6 (from circle C).

From the options, only -18 is odd, negative, and multiple of 6.

9) Answer: D.

let x be total number of cards in the box, then number of red cards is: $x - 144$

The probability of choosing a red card is one third. Then: probability$= \frac{1}{3} = \frac{x-144}{x}$

Use cross multiplication to solve for x.

$x \times 1 = 3(x - 144) \to x = 3x - 432 \to 3x - x = 432 \to x = 216$

10) Answer: C.

Plug in the values of x in each equation and check.

I. $(-2)^2 - 3(-2) + 5 = 4 + 6 + 5 = 15 \neq 0$

   $(1)^2 - 3(1) + 5 = 1 - 3 + 5 = 3 \neq 0$

II. $3(-2)^2 + 3(-2) = 12 - 6 = 6 \to 6 = 6$

   $3(1)^2 + 3(1) = 3 + 3 = 6 \to 6 = 6$

III. $2(-2)^2 + 2(-2) - 4 = 8 - 4 - 4 = 0 = 0$

   $2(1)^2 + 2(1) - 4 = 2 + 2 - 4 = 0 = 0$

Equations II and III are correct.

11) Answer: B.

Number of biology book: 50; Total number of books; $50 + 68 + 82 = 200$

the ratio of the number of biology books to the total number of books is: $\frac{50}{200} = \frac{1}{4}$

12) Answer: D.

A. $f(x) = x^2 + 2$; if $x = 1 \to f(1) = (1)^2 + 2 = 1 + 2 = 3 \neq 4$

B. $f(x) = x^2 - 2$; if $x = 1 \to f(1) = (1)^2 - 2 = 1 - 2 = -1 \neq 4$

C. $f(x) = \sqrt{x + 3}$ if $x = 1 \to f(1) = \sqrt{1 + 3} = \sqrt{4} = 2 \neq 4$

D. $f(x) = \sqrt{x} + 3$ if $x = 1 \to f(1) = \sqrt{1} + 3 = 4 = 4$

Choice D is correct.

13) Answer: B.

$\alpha = 180° - 128° = 52°$

$\beta = 180° - 115° = 65°$

$x + \alpha + \beta = 180° \to$

$x = 180° - 52° - 65° = 63°$

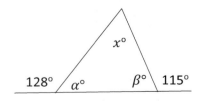

14) Answer: C.

$(4^a)^b = 256 \rightarrow 4^{ab} = 256$

$256 = 4^4 \rightarrow 4^{ab} = 4^4 \rightarrow ab = 4$

15) Answer: C.

$\sqrt{x} = 5 \rightarrow x = 25$ then; $\sqrt{x} - 9 = \sqrt{25} - 9 = 5 - 9 = -4$

and $\sqrt{x - 9} = \sqrt{25 - 9} = \sqrt{16} = 4$

Then: $(\sqrt{x - 9}) + (\sqrt{x} - 9) = 4 + (-4) = 0$

16) Answer: A.

All integers from 15 to 21 are: 15, 16, 17, 18, 19, 20, 21.

The mean of these integers is: $\frac{15+16+17+18+19+20+21}{7} = \frac{126}{7} = 18$

17) Answer: C.

$-3a + 5a + 7a = 63 \rightarrow 9a = 63 \rightarrow a = \frac{63}{9} = 7$

Then; $\frac{7a-1}{6} = \frac{7(7)-1}{6} = \frac{49-1}{6} = 8$

18) Answer: B.

$|-16 - 7| - |-12 + 3| = |-23| - |-9| = 23 - 9 = 14$

19) Answer: B.

let x be the number of gallons of water the container holds when it is full. Then;

$\frac{8}{35}x = 1.6 \rightarrow x = \frac{35 \times 1.6}{8} = 7$

20) Answer: D.

Based on the table provided: $g(-2) = g(x = -2) = 3$

$g(4) = g(x = 4) = -4$

$4g(-2) - 2g(4) = 4(3) - 2(-4) = 12 + 8 = 20$

21) Answer: D.

Choose a random number for a and check the options. Let a be equal to 21 which is divisible by 7, then:

    A. $a - 4 = 21 - 4 = 17$ is not divisible by 5.

    B. $a + 4 = 21 + 4 = 25$ is divisible by 5.

but if $a = 7 \rightarrow a + 4 = 12$ is not divisible by 5.

C. $4a = 4 \times 21 = 84$ is divisible by 5.

D. $5a - 5 = (5 \times 21) - 5 = 100$ is divisible by 5.

22) Answer: B.

$(x - 3)^2 = 9 \rightarrow$ Find the third root of both sides. Then: $x - 3 = 3 \rightarrow x = 6$

$\rightarrow (x - 2)(x - 5) = (6 - 2)(6 - 5) = (4)(1) = 4$

23) Answer: C.

The quadrilateral is a trapezoid. Use the formula of the area of trapezoids: $Area = \frac{1}{2}h(b_1 + b_2)$

You can find the height of the trapezoid by finding the difference of the values of y for the points A and D. (or points B and C)

$h = 9 - 3 = 6$

AB$= \sqrt{(x_1 - x_2)^2 + (y_1 - y_2)^2} = \sqrt{(6 - 4)^2 + (9 - 9)^2} = \sqrt{4 + 0} = 2$

CD$= \sqrt{(x_1 - x_2)^2 + (y_1 - y_2)^2} = \sqrt{(7 - 1)^2 + (3 - 3)^2} = \sqrt{36 + 0} = 6$

Area of the trapezoid is: $\frac{1}{2}h(b_1 + b_2) = \frac{1}{2}(6)(2 + 6) = 24$

24) Answer: C.

The value of y in the x-intercept of a line is zero. Then:

$y = 0 \rightarrow 5x - 3(0) = 8 \rightarrow 5x = 8 \rightarrow x = \frac{8}{5}$ then, x-intercept of the line is $\frac{8}{5}$.

25) Answer: A.

Formula of triangle area $= \frac{1}{2}$ (base × height)

Since the angles are $45°, 45°, 90°$, then this is an isosceles triangle, meaning that the base and height of the triangle are equal.

Triangle area $= \frac{1}{2}$ (base × height) $= \frac{1}{2}(10 \times 10) = 50$

26) Answer: A.

Let x be the number of years. Therefore, $3,000 per year equals $3,000x$. Starting from $19,000 annual salary means you should add that amount to $3,000x$.

Income more than that is: $I > 3,000x + 19,000$

27) Answer: D.

The amount of money for x bookshelf is: $200x$

Then, the total cost of all bookshelves is equal to: $200x + 500$

The total cost, in dollar, per bookshelf is: $\frac{Total\ cost}{number\ of\ items} = \frac{200x + 500}{x}$

28) Answer: A.

$|x - 3| \geq 12$

Then: $x - 3 \geq 12 \rightarrow x \geq 12 + 3 \rightarrow x \geq 15$

Or $x - 3 \leq -12 \rightarrow x \leq -12 + 3 \rightarrow x \leq -9$

Then, the solution is: $x \geq 15 \ \cup \ x \leq -9$

29) Answer: B.

Since E is the midpoint of AB, then the area of all triangles DAE, DEF, CFE and CBE are equal.

Let x be the area of one of the triangles, then: $4x = 120 \rightarrow$

$x = 30$

The area of DEC $= 2x = 2(30) = 60$

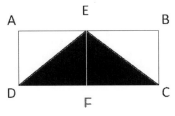

30) Answer: A.

$5 < -4x - 3 < 13 \rightarrow$ Add 3 to all sides. $5 + 3 < -4x - 3 + 3 < 13 + 3$

$\rightarrow 8 < -4x < 16 \rightarrow$ Divide all sides by -4.

(Remember that when you divide all sides of an inequality by a negative number, the inequality sign will be swapped. $<$ becomes $>$)

$\frac{8}{-4} > \frac{-4x}{-4} > \frac{16}{-6} \rightarrow -2 > x > -4, or\ -4 < x < -2$

"End"

Made in the USA
Middletown, DE
17 June 2024

55958498R00102